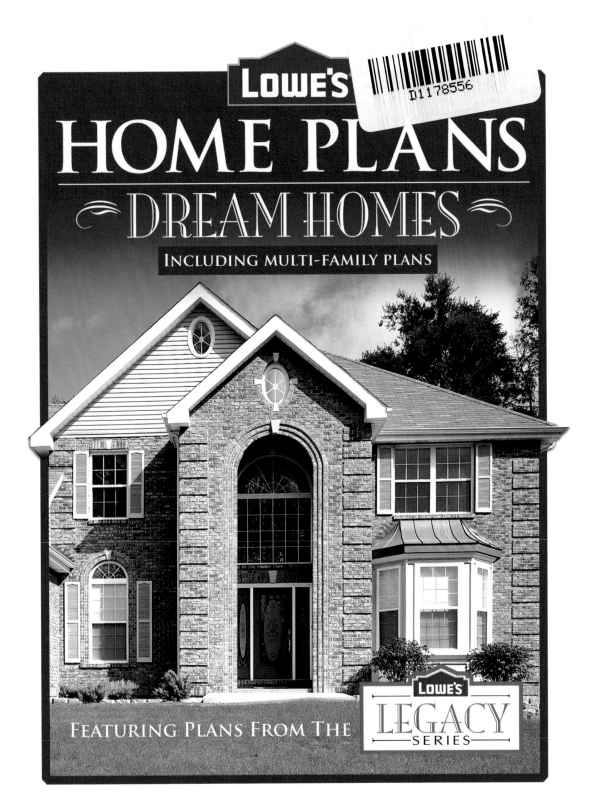

LOWE'S

HOME PLANS

~ DREAM HOMES ~

INCLUDING MULTI-FAMILY PLANS

FEATURING PLANS FROM THE

LOWE'S
LEGACY
SERIES

HDA
INC

COVER HOME - The house shown on the front cover is Plan 536-007D-0006 and is featured on page 11. Photo courtesy of Dublin Homes, St. Louis, Missouri Photographer: Michael Marxer

LOWE'S LEGACY SERIES: DREAM HOME PLANS is published by HDA, Inc., 944 Anglum Road, St. Louis, MO, 63042. All rights reserved. Reproduction in whole or in part without written permission of the publisher is prohibited. Printed in U.S.A. © 2009. Artist drawings and photos shown in this publication may vary slightly from the actual working drawings. Some photos are shown in mirror reverse. Please refer to the floor plan for accurate layout.

ISBN-13: 978-1-58678-063-0
ISBN-10: 1-58678-063-8

Current Printing

10 9 8 7 6 5 4 3

HDA, Inc.
944 Anglum Rd.
St. Louis, Missouri 63042
corporate website - www.hdainc.com
www.houseplansandmore.com

CONTENTS

It's what separates you from the have knots.

We understand that it is difficult to find blueprints for a home that will meet all your needs. That is why HDA, Inc. is pleased to offer home plan modification services.

Typical home plan modifications include:

- Changing foundation type
- Adding square footage to a plan
- Changing the entry into a garage
- Changing a two-car garage to a three-car garage or making a garage larger
- Redesigning kitchen, baths, and bedrooms
- Changing exterior elevations
- Or most other home plan modifications

Home plan modifications we cannot make include:

- Reversing the plans
- Adapting/engineering plans to meet your local building codes
- Combining parts of two different plans (due to copyright laws)

Our plan modification service is easy to use. Simply:

1. Decide on the modifications you want. For the most accurate quote, be as detailed as possible and refer to rooms in the same manner as the floor plan (i.e. if the floor plan refers to a "den" then use "den" in your description). Including a sketch of the modified floor plan is always helpful.

2. Complete and e-mail the modification request form that can be found online at www.houseplansandmore.com.

3. Within two business days, you will receive your quote. Quotes do not include the cost of the reproducible masters required for our designer to legally make changes.

4. Call to accept the quote and purchase the reproducible masters. For example, if your quote is $850 and the reproducible masters for your plan are $800, your order total will be $1650 plus two shipping and handling charges (one to ship the reproducible masters to our designer and one to ship the modified plans to you).

5. Our designer will send you up to three drafts to verify your initial changes. Extra costs apply after the third draft. If additional changes are made that alter the original request, extra charges may be incurred.

6. Once you approve a draft with the final changes, we then make the changes to the reproducible masters by adding additional sheets. The original reproducible masters (with no changes) plus your new changed sheets will be shipped to you.

Other Important Information:

- Plans cannot be redrawn in reverse format. All modifications will be made to match the reproducible master's original layout. Once you receive the plans, you can make reverse copies at your local blueprint shop.

- Our staff designer will provide the first draft for your review within 4 weeks (plus shipping time) of receiving your order.

- You will receive up to three drafts to review before your original changes are modified. The first draft will totally encompass all modifications based on your original request. Additional changes not included in your original request will be charged separately at an hourly rate of $75 or a flat quoted rate.

- Modifications will be drawn on a separate sheet with the changes shown and a note to see the main sheet for details. For example, a floor plan sheet from the original set (i.e. Sheet 3) would be followed by a new floor plan sheet with changes (i.e. Sheet A-3).

- Plans are drawn to meet national building codes. Modifications will not be drawn to any particular state or county codes, thus we cannot guarantee that the revisions will meet your local building codes. You may be required to have a local architect or designer review the plans in order to have them comply with your state or county building codes.

- Time and cost estimates are good for 90 calendar days.

- All modification requests need to be submitted in writing. Verbal requests will not be accepted.

2 EASY STEPS FOR FAST SERVICE

1. Visit www.houseplansandmore.com to download the modification request form

2. E-mail the completed form to customize@hdainc.com or fax to 913-856-7751

If you are not able to access the internet, please call 1-877-379-3420 (Monday-Friday, 8am-5pm CST)

Choosing a home plan is an exciting but difficult task. Many factors play a role in what home plan is best for you and your family. To help you get started, we have pinpointed some of the major factors to consider when searching for your dream home. Take the time to evaluate your family's needs and you will have an easier time sorting through all of the home plans offered in this book.

BUDGET: The first thing to consider is your budget. Many items take part in this budget, from ordering the blueprints to the last doorknob purchased. Once you have found your dream home plan, visit our website at www.houseplansandmore.com to get a cost-to-build estimate to ensure that the finished product is still within your cost range.

FAMILY LIFESTYLE: After your budget is deciphered, you need to assess you and your family's lifestyle needs. Think about the stage of life you are at now, and what stages you will be going through in the future. Ask yourself questions to figure out how much room you need now and if you will need room for expansion. Are you married? Do you have children? How many children do you plan on having? Are you an empty-nester?

Incorporate in your planning any frequent guests you may have, including elderly parents, grandchildren or adult children who may live with you.

Does your family entertain a lot? If so, think about the rooms you will need to do so. Will you need both formal and informal spaces? Do you need a gourmet kitchen? Do you need a game room and/or a wet bar?

FLOOR PLAN LAYOUTS: When looking through our home plans, imagine yourself walking through the house. Consider the flow from the entry to the living, sleeping and gathering areas. Does the layout ensure privacy for the master bedroom? Does the garage enter near the kitchen for easy unloading? Does the placement of the windows provide enough privacy from any neighboring properties? Do you plan on using furniture you already have? Will this furniture fit in the appropriate rooms? When you find a plan you want to purchase, be sure to picture yourself actually living in it.

Experts in the field suggest that the best way to determine your needs is to begin by listing everything you like or dislike about your current home.

EXTERIOR SPACES: There are many different home styles ranging from Traditional to Contemporary. Flip through and find which style most appeals to you and the neighborhood in which you plan to build. Also think of your site and how the entire house will fit on this site. Picture any landscaping you plan on incorporating into the design. Using your imagination is key when choosing a home plan.

Choosing a home plan can be an intimidating experience. Asking yourself these questions before you get started on the search will help you through the process. With our large selection of multiple styles we are certain you will find your dream home in the following pages.

THE LOWE'S LEGACY SERIES

LEG·A·CY: SOMETHING THAT IS HANDED DOWN OR REMAINS FOR GENERATIONS

HDA, Inc. is proud to introduce to you the Lowe's Legacy Series. The home plans in this collection carry on the Lowe's tradition of quality and expertise, and will continue to do so for many generations.

Choosing a home plan can be a daunting task. With the Legacy Series, we will set your mind at ease. Selecting a plan from this group will ensure a home designed with the Lowe's standard of excellence, creating a dream home for you and your family.

This collection of Legacy Series plans includes our most popular dream home plans. Browse through the pages to discover a home with the options and special characteristics you need.

Along with one-of-a-kind craftsmanship, all Legacy Series home plans offer industry-leading material lists. These accurate material lists will save you a considerable amount of time and money, providing you with the quantity, dimensions and descriptions of the major building materials necessary to construct your home. You'll get faster and more accurate bids from your contractor while saving money by paying for only the materials you need.

The Lowe's Legacy Series is the perfect place to start your search for the home of your dreams. You will find the expected beauty you want and the functional efficiency you need, all designed with unmatched quality.

Turn the page and begin the wonderful journey of finding your new home.

Photos clockwise from top: 536-053D-0017, page 16; 536-027D-0014, page 21; 536-065L-0229, page 40; 536-001D-0012, page 46.

SPECIAL FEATURES

2,959 total square feet of living area

A beamed ceiling tops the great room plus a fireplace and built-ins decorate one wall

A breakfast area, sitting area and stylish kitchen create a family center perfect for casual gatherings

A library with built-in shelving and angled walls provides an area dedicated for organized work at home

3 bedrooms, 2 1/2 baths, 3-car side entry garage

Walk-out basement foundation

Interior View - Great Room

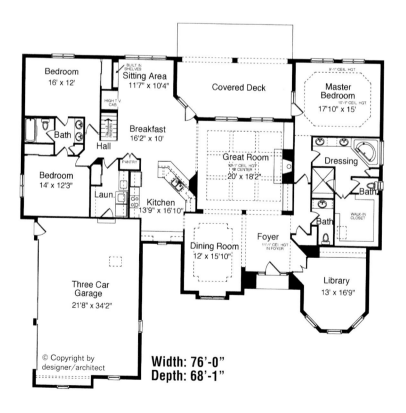

Bedroom
16' x 12'

BUILT IN
SHELVES
Sitting Area
11'7" x 10'4"

Covered Deck

9'1" CEIL. HGT
Master Bedroom
17'-1" CEIL. HGT
17'10" x 15'

HIGH T.V.
CAB.

Bath

Hall

Breakfast
16'2" x 10'

Great Room
12'-1" CEIL. HGT
@ CENTER
20' x 18'2"

Dressing

Bath

Bedroom
14' x 12'3"

PANTRY

Laun.

Kitchen
13'9" x 16'10"

WALK-IN
CLOSET

Bath

Dining Room
12' x 15'10"

Foyer
11'-1" CEIL. HGT
IN FOYER

Bath

Three Car Garage
21'8" x 34'2"

Library
13' x 16'9"

© Copyright by
designer/architect

Width: 76'-0"
Depth: 68'-1"

SPECIAL FEATURES

3,169 total square feet of living area

Formal areas include an enormous entry with handcrafted stairway and powder room, French doors to the living room and an open dining area with tray ceiling

Informal areas consist of a large family room with a bay window, fireplace, walk-in wet bar and kitchen open to the breakfast room

Stylish master bedroom is located on the second floor for privacy

Bedroom #3 includes a private study

4 bedrooms, 2 1/2 baths, 3-car side entry garage

Basement foundation

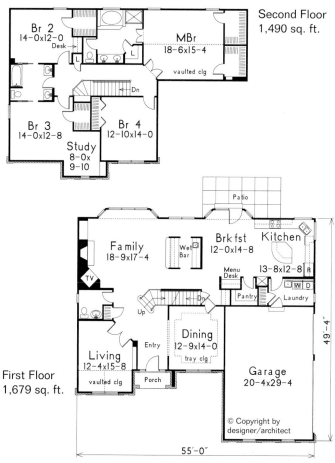

Second Floor
1,490 sq. ft.

Br 2
14-0x12-0
Desk

MBr
18-6x15-4
vaulted clg

Br 3
14-0x12-8

Br 4
12-10x14-0

Study
8-0x
9-10

Dn

First Floor
1,679 sq. ft.

Patio

Family
18-9x17-4

Wet Bar

Brk fst
12-0x14-8

Kitchen
13-8x12-8

TV

Menu Desk

Pantry

W D
Laundry

Up

Dn

Dining
12-9x14-0
tray clg

Living
12-4x15-8
vaulted clg

Entry

Porch

Garage
20-4x29-4

49'-4"

55'-0"

© Copyright by designer/architect

SPECIAL FEATURES

3,687 total square feet of living area

Energy efficient home with
2" x 6" exterior walls

A magnificent circular staircase
winds down to greet you as you
enter this Tuscan style home

The two-story ceiling and fireplace flanked
by built-in cabinets in the great room create
an atmosphere that's perfect for entertaining

The spacious kitchen features a large
eat-in island and direct access to the
formal dining room and laundry

4 bedrooms, 3 1/2 baths,
3-car side entry garage

Walk-out basement foundation

Rear View

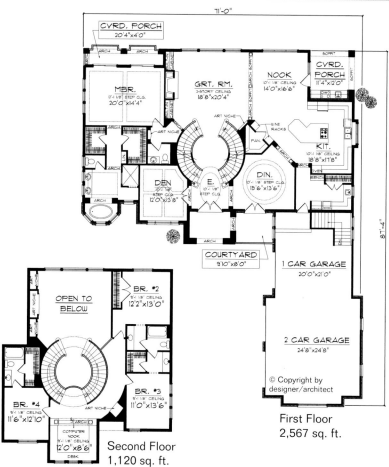

First Floor
2,567 sq. ft.

Second Floor
1,120 sq. ft.

LEGACY SERIES

SPECIAL FEATURES

2,624 total square feet of living area

Dramatic two-story foyer opens to a bayed dining room through a classic colonnade

Magnificent great room with 18' ceiling is brightly lit with palladian windows

Master bedroom includes bay window, walk-in closets, plant shelves and a sunken bath

4 bedrooms, 2 1/2 baths, 2-car side entry garage

Basement foundation

Second Floor
850 sq. ft.

First Floor
1,774 sq. ft.

Interior View - Master Bath

SPECIAL FEATURES

2,858 total square feet of living area

Energy efficient home with
2" x 6" exterior walls

A large island in the kitchen provides plenty
of workspace when preparing meals as
well as a double sink for added function

The see-through fireplace separates
the great room and the outdoor porch,
warming the home inside and out

The spacious and relaxing owner's
bedroom suite offers an enormous
closet, double-bowl vanity, amazing
walk-in shower and a spa style tub

3 bedrooms, 3 1/2 baths, 3-car garage

Walk-out basement foundation

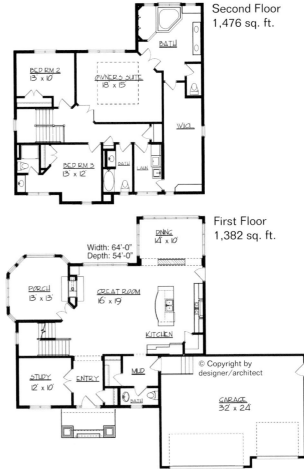

Second Floor
1,476 sq. ft.

BATH

BED RM 2
13' x 10'

OWNERS SUITE
18 x 15

WIC

BED RM 3
13' x 12'

BATH

LAUN

First Floor
1,382 sq. ft.

DINING
14' x 10'

Width: 64'-0"
Depth: 54'-0"

PORCH
13' x 13'

GREAT ROOM
16' x 19'

KITCHEN

STUDY
12' x 10'

ENTRY

MUD

BATH

© Copyright by
designer/architect

GARAGE
32' x 24'

SPECIAL FEATURES

2,940 total square feet of living area

Two sets of twin dormers add outdoor charm while lighting the indoors

Massive central foyer leads into the sunken living room below and has access to the second floor attic

Private master bedroom is complete with its own bath featuring a luxurious corner tub and large walk-in closet

A novel bridge provides a view of the sunken living room below and access to the second floor attic

4 bedrooms, 3 baths, 2-car side entry garage

Basement foundation

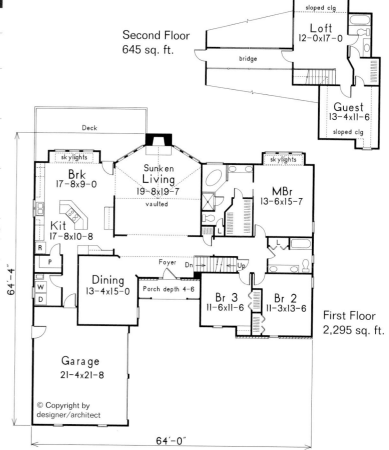

Second Floor
645 sq. ft.

sloped clg

Loft
12-0x17-0

bridge

Guest
13-4x11-6

sloped clg

Deck

skylights

Brk
17-8x9-0

Sunken
Living
19-8x19-7
vaulted

skylights

MBr
13-6x15-7

Kit
17-8x10-8

R

P

W

D

Dining
13-4x15-0

Foyer   Dn

Porch depth 4-6

Up

Br 3
11-6x11-6

Br 2
11-3x13-6

First Floor
2,295 sq. ft.

Garage
21-4x21-8

© Copyright by
designer/architect

64'-4"

64'-0"

LEGACY SERIES

SPECIAL FEATURES

5,143 total square feet of living area

Energy efficient home with
2" x 6" exterior walls

The first floor includes a grand foyer
and library both with custom cabinetry
and an impressive master bedroom with
lavish dressing area and walk-in closet

The second floor bedrooms all have
walk-in closets and 9' ceilings

The optional lower level offers an additional
1,351 square feet of living area and
includes a sitting room with fireplace, media
center, wine storage and exercise room

4 bedrooms, 3 1/2 baths,
3-car side entry garage

Walk-out basement foundation

Interior View - Media Room

Second Floor
1,820 sq. ft.

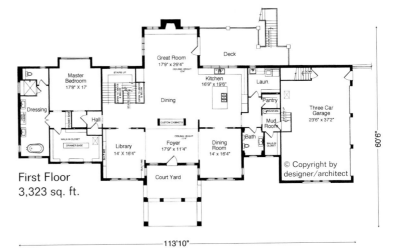

First Floor
3,323 sq. ft.

© Copyright by
designer/architect

Second Floor
710 sq. ft.

SPECIAL FEATURES

2,525 total square feet of living area

Energy efficient home with
2" x 6" exterior walls

Spacious living room flaunts a
fabulous fireplace, a soaring vaulted
ceiling and a striking window wall

Second floor balcony is warmed
by an overhead skylight

An efficient and open kitchen is
perfect for easy meal preparation

First floor bedroom is convenient and
would make a great master bedroom

3 bedrooms, 2 baths, 2-car
tandem drive under garage

Walk-out basement foundation

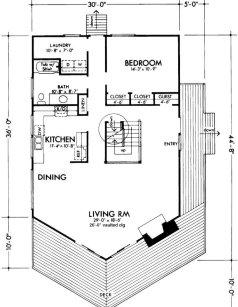

First Floor
1,210 sq. ft.

© Copyright by
designer/architect

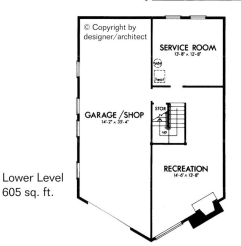

Lower Level
605 sq. ft.

SPECIAL FEATURES

2,529 total square feet of living area

Distinguished appearance enhances this home's classic interior arrangement

Bonus room over the garage, which is included in the square footage, has direct access from the attic and the second floor hall

A private bath with garden tub, walk-in closet and coffered ceiling enhance the master bedroom suite

4 bedrooms, 2 1/2 baths, 2-car garage

Basement foundation

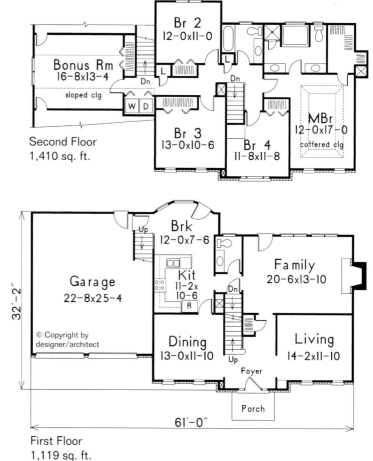

Second Floor
1,410 sq. ft.

Bonus Rm
16-8x13-4
sloped clg

Br 2
12-0x11-0

Br 3
13-0x10-6

Br 4
11-8x11-8

MBr
12-0x17-0
coffered clg

W D

First Floor
1,119 sq. ft.

Garage
22-8x25-4

Brk
12-0x7-6

Kit
11-2x10-6

Family
20-6x13-10

Dining
13-0x11-10

Living
14-2x11-10

Foyer

Porch

32'-2"

61'-0"

© Copyright by designer/architect

SPECIAL FEATURES

3,195 total square feet of living area

Energy efficient home with
2" x 8" exterior walls

Step into this stunning two-story and
catch a view of the grand staircase flanked
by the formal living and dining rooms

A butler's pantry bridges the
kitchen and the dining room for easy
serving during dinner parties

The master suite offers the option of having
French doors leading into a sitting area or
this area could be used as a fourth bedroom

4 bedrooms, 2 1/2 baths, 3-car garage

Basement foundation

Second Floor
1,437 sq. ft.

Br 3
15—8x11—6

open to below

shelf

DN

M Suite
12—8x18—6

Br 4/
Sitting
11x10—6

open to below

shelf

Br 2
15—8x13—4

window seat

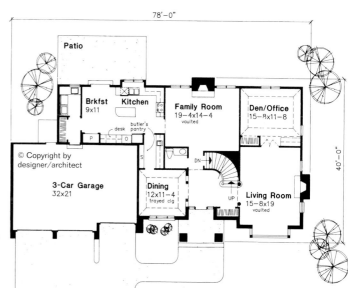

78'—0"

Patio

Brkfst
9x11

Kitchen

Family Room
19—4x14—4
vaulted

Den/Office
15—8x11—8

butler's
pantry

desk

P

© Copyright by
designer/architect

3-Car Garage
32x21

Dining
12x11—4
trayed clg

DN

UP

Living Room
15—8x19
vaulted

40'—0"

First Floor
1,758 sq. ft.

LEGACY SERIES

SPECIAL FEATURES

3,861 total square feet of living area

Detailed brickwork surrounding the arched windows and quoined corners create a timeless exterior

Two-story great room has a large fireplace, flanking bookshelves, massive window wall and balcony overlook

The state-of-the-art kitchen has an island cooktop, built-in oven/microwave oven, large pantry, and menu desk

A coffered ceiling, bay window, two walk-in closets and a huge bath adorn the master bedroom

4 bedrooms, 3 1/2 baths, 3-car side entry garage

Walk-out basement foundation

Interior View - Kitchen

Second Floor
1,064 sq. ft.

First Floor
2,797 sq. ft.

SPECIAL FEATURES

2,356 total square feet of living area

Impressive arched and mullioned
window treatment embellishes
the entrance and foyer

Bedroom #4 is located above the side
entry garage and has access to the attic

Full-size laundry facility

Adjoining family room, breakfast area and
kitchen form an extensive living area

4 bedrooms, 2 1/2 baths,
2-car side entry garage

Basement foundation

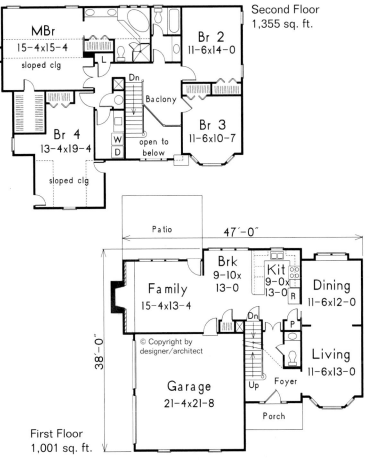

Second Floor
1,355 sq. ft.

MBr
15-4x15-4
sloped clg

Br 2
11-6x14-0

Dn

Br 4
13-4x19-4

Baclony

Br 3
11-6x10-7

W
D

open to
below

sloped clg

Patio

47'-0"

Brk
9-10x
13-0

Kit
9-0x
13-0

Dining
11-6x12-0

Family
15-4x13-4

R

Dn

© Copyright by
designer/architect

P

38'-0"

Living
11-6x13-0

Garage
21-4x21-8

Up

Foyer

Porch

First Floor
1,001 sq. ft.

SPECIAL FEATURES

3,138 total square feet of living area

Impressive staircase descends into the large entry and through double-doors to the study

The private dining room is spacious and secluded

Master bedroom, family and laundry rooms are among the many generously sized rooms

Three large bedrooms, two baths and four walk-in closets compose the second floor

4 bedrooms, 3 1/2 baths, 2-car side entry garage

Basement foundation

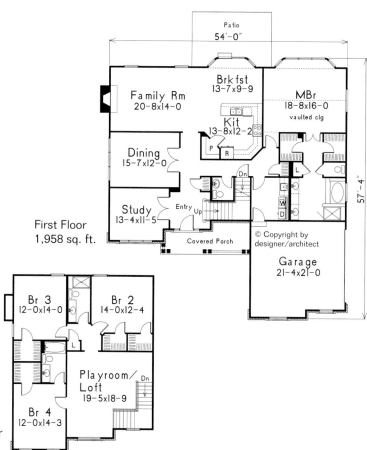

Patio
54'-0"

Brkfst
13-7x9-9

Family Rm
20-8x14-0

MBr
18-8x16-0
vaulted clg

Kit
13-8x12-2

Dining
15-7x12-0

Study
13-4x11-5

Entry
Up

Dn

P   R

L

W
D

First Floor
1,958 sq. ft.

Covered Porch

© Copyright by
designer/architect

Garage
21-4x21-0

57'-4"

Br 3
12-0x14-0

Br 2
14-0x12-4

L

Playroom/
Loft
19-5x18-9

Dn

Br 4
12-0x14-3

Second Floor
1,180 sq. ft.

SPECIAL FEATURES

4,288 total square feet of living area

The master bedroom features a deluxe bath with a double vanity, large tub, his and her walk-in closets, and a linen closet

The hearth room offers a great amount of light and a fireplace that serves as a cozy gathering area

Each bedroom is spacious in size and has its own walk-in closet

4 bedrooms, 3 1/2 baths, 3-car side entry garage

Basement foundation

Rear View

Second Floor
1,744 sq. ft.

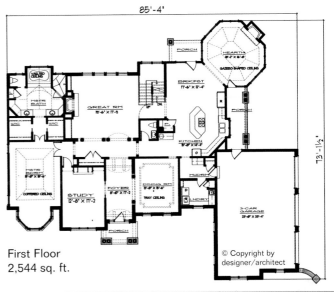

First Floor
2,544 sq. ft.

SPECIAL FEATURES

3,116 total square feet of living area

Arched mullioned windows provide balance across the impressive facade

First floor master bedroom and bedroom #2 on the second floor have private baths and walk-in closets

Bonus room above the garage, which is included in the square footage, is available for future use

Vaulted ceiling and balcony add even more spaciousness

4 bedrooms, 3 1/2 baths, 2-car side entry garage

Basement foundation

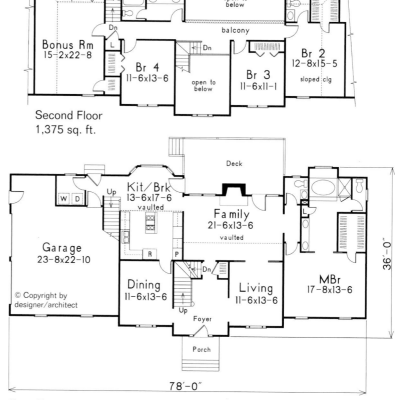

Second Floor
1,375 sq. ft.

Bonus Rm
15-2x22-8

Br 4
11-6x13-6

Br 3
11-6x11-1

Br 2
12-8x15-5

sloped clg

open to below

balcony

Dn

open to below

First Floor
1,741 sq. ft.

Deck

Kit/Brk
13-6x17-6
vaulted

Family
21-6x13-6
vaulted

Garage
23-8x22-10

Dining
11-6x13-6

Living
11-6x13-6

MBr
17-8x13-6

Foyer

Porch

78'-0"

36'-0"

© Copyright by designer/architect

SPECIAL FEATURES

3,113 total square feet of living area

Energy efficient home with
2" x 6" exterior walls

A see-through fireplace warms both the
formal living room and casual family room

The chef of the family will love this
gourmet kitchen complete with
an abundance of counterspace, a
stovetop island and walk-in pantry

The nook/sun room with access to a
screen porch allows the family to enjoy
the great outdoors all year long

4 bedrooms, 2 1/2 baths, 3-car garage

Basement foundation

Interior View - Living Room

Second Floor
956 sq. ft.

BR.#3
13'0" X 13'0"

BR.#2
12'6" X 13'6"

LOFT

BR.#4
11'4" X 13'0"

OPEN TO
E.

PLANT LEDGE

LINEN

First Floor
2,157 sq. ft.

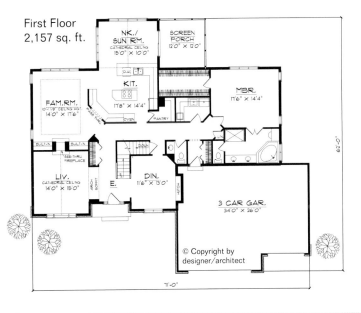

NK./
SUN RM.
CATHEDRAL CEILING
15'0" X 10'0"

SCREEN
PORCH
12'0" X 12'0"

KIT.
17'8" X 14'4"

MBR.
17'6" X 14'4"

FAM.RM.
10' 1/8" CEILING HGT
14'0" X 17'6"

PANTRY

SEE-THRU
FIREPLACE

LIV.
CATHEDRAL CEILING
14'0" X 15'0"

DIN.
11'6" X 13'0"

E.

3 CAR GAR.
34'0" X 26'0"

62'-0"

71'-0"

© Copyright by
designer/architect

SPECIAL FEATURES

4,562 total square feet of living area

The cozy hearth room and master bedroom showcase tray ceilings and moldings

A dressing area, deluxe bath and extra-large walk-in closet crown the master bedroom

The kitchen with island opens to the breakfast and hearth rooms for an open atmosphere

4 bedrooms, 3 1/2 baths, 3-car side entry garage

Basement foundation

Second Floor
1,198 sq. ft.

First Floor
3,364 sq. ft.

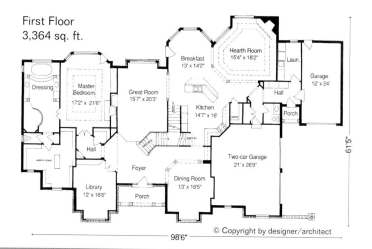

© Copyright by designer/architect

SPECIAL FEATURES

2,808 total square feet of living area

An impressive front exterior showcases
three porches for quiet times

Large living and dining rooms
flank an elegant entry

Bedroom #3 shares a porch with the living
room and a spacious bath with bedroom #2

Vaulted master bedroom enjoys
a secluded screened porch and
sumptuous bath with corner tub,
double vanities and huge walk-in closet

Living room can easily convert to
an optional fourth bedroom

3 bedrooms, 2 1/2 baths,
3-car side entry garage

Basement foundation

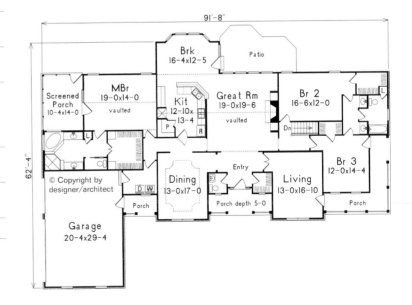

SPECIAL FEATURES

3,718 total square feet of living area

Energy efficient home with
2" x 6" exterior walls

The cheerful kitchen has a double-bowl
sink in the angular island, a large pantry
and opens up nicely to the dinette area

The majestic great room has a center
fireplace flanked by bookshelves

The relaxing owner's bedroom
offers a generous closet, double-
bowl vanity, amazing walk-in shower
and a pampering whirlpool tub

5 bedrooms, 3 1/2 baths, 3-car garage

Walk-out basement foundation

Second Floor
1,770 sq. ft.

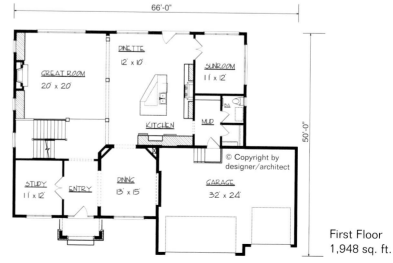

© Copyright by
designer/architect

First Floor
1,948 sq. ft.

SPECIAL FEATURES

2,100 total square feet of living area

The vaulted great room enjoys the warmth of a gas fireplace flanked by shelves

Every bedroom features a walk-in closet helping to keep everything organized

Shelves and extra storage can be found in the garage

Bonus room above the garage has an additional 317 square feet of living area

4 bedrooms, 2 1/2 baths, 2-car side entry garage

Slab foundation, drawings also include crawl space foundation

Rear View

Optional Second Floor

Attic Access

Bonus Bath

Clos.

Sloped Clg.

Future Bonus Room
13-2 x 12-6
8' Clg. Ht.

DN

Shwr. | Linen

First Floor
2,100 sq. ft.

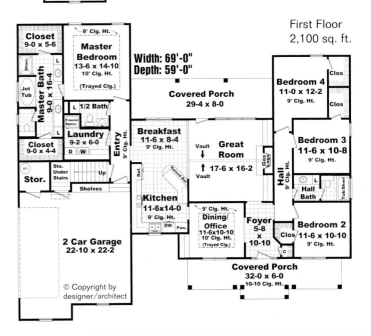

Closet
9-0 x 5-6

Master Bedroom
13-6 x 14-10
10' Clg. Ht.
(Trayed Clg.)

Width: 69'-0"
Depth: 59'-0"

Master Bath
9-0 x 16-4

Jet Tub

L 1/2 Bath

Freezer Space

Laundry
9-2 x 6-0
D | W

Closet
9-0 x 4-4

Sto. Under Stairs

Stor.

Up

Shelves

Entry
9' Clg. Ht.

Covered Porch
29-4 x 8-0

Breakfast
11-6 x 8-4
9' Clg. Ht.

Vault

Great Room
17-6 x 16-2
Vault

Gas Logs

Kitchen
11-6x14-0
9' Clg. Ht.

DW | Pan.

Ref.

Raised Br.

Dining/Office
11-6x10-10
10' Clg. Ht.
(Trayed Clg.)

Foyer
5-8 x 10-10

Bedroom 4
11-0 x 12-2
9' Clg. Ht.

Clos

Clos

Bedroom 3
11-6 x 10-8
9' Clg. Ht.

Hall
9' Clg. Ht.

Hall Bath

Tub/Shwr.

Bedroom 2
11-6 x 10-10
9' Clg. Ht.

Clos

2 Car Garage
22-10 x 22-2

Covered Porch
32-0 x 6-0
10-10 Clg. Ht.

© Copyright by designer/architect

SPECIAL FEATURES

4,328 total square feet of living area

The extra-large gourmet kitchen and breakfast room offer a spacious area for chores and family gatherings, while providing a striking view through the great room to the fireplace wall

For convenience, a butler's pantry is located in the hall leading to the dining room

An extravagant master bedroom and library round out the first floor

The lavish lower level includes a media room, billiard room, exercise room and two bedrooms

3 bedrooms, 3 1/2 baths, 3-car side entry garage

Walk-out basement foundation

Interior View - Foyer

First Floor
2,582 sq. ft.

© Copyright by designer/architect

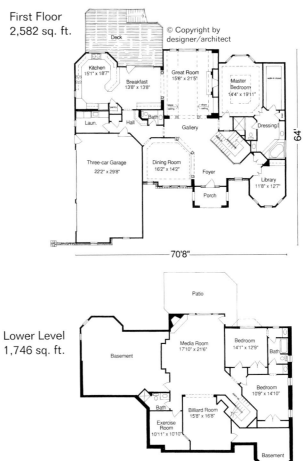

Lower Level
1,746 sq. ft.

SPECIAL FEATURES

2,401 total square feet of living area

Striking front facade with handsome main entry and brick quoins

Master bedroom has an elegant double-door entry, two walk-in closets and a deluxe bath

Full bay windows located on both floors create a great view from the rear of this home

Spacious kitchen features a vaulted ceiling, double pantry, a large work island and planning center

3 bedrooms, 2 1/2 baths, 2-car garage

Basement foundation, drawings also include slab and crawl space foundations

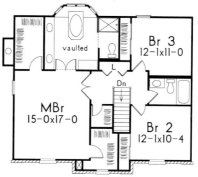

Second Floor
1,046 sq. ft.

vaulted

Br 3
12-1x11-0

MBr
15-0x17-0

Dn

Br 2
12-1x10-4

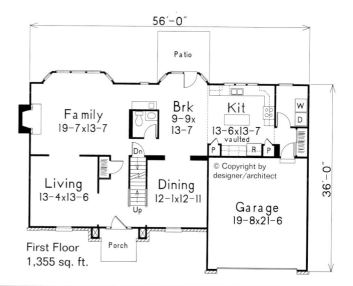

56'-0"

Patio

Family
19-7x13-7

Brk
9-9x
13-7

Kit
13-6x13-7
vaulted

W
D

Dn

Living
13-4x13-6

Dining
12-1x12-11

Up

© Copyright by
designer/architect

Garage
19-8x21-6

36'-0"

First Floor
1,355 sq. ft.

Porch

SPECIAL FEATURES

2,523 total square feet of living area

Entry with high ceiling leads to massive
vaulted great room with wet bar,
plant shelves, pillars and fireplace
with a harmonious window trio

Elaborate kitchen with bay and
breakfast bar adjoins the morning
room with a fireplace-in-a-bay

Vaulted master bedroom features a
fireplace, book and plant shelves, large
walk-in closet and double baths

3 bedrooms, 2 baths, 3-car garage

Basement foundation, drawings also
include crawl space and slab foundations

Rear View

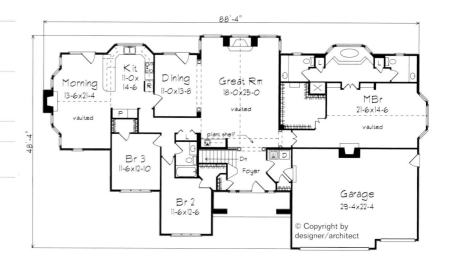

88'-4"

48'-4"

Morning
13-6x21-4
vaulted

Kit
11-0x
14-6

Dining
11-0x13-8

Great Rm
18-0x25-0
vaulted

MBr
21-6x14-6
vaulted

plant shelf

Br 3
11-6x12-10

Dn
Foyer

Br 2
11-6x12-6

Garage
29-4x22-4

LEGACY SERIES

SPECIAL FEATURES

2,869 total square feet of living area

Foyer, flanked by columned living and dining rooms, leads to the vaulted family room with a fireplace and twin sets of French doors

10' ceilings on the first floor and 9' ceilings on the second floor

4 bedrooms, 3 baths, 2-car rear entry garage

Slab foundation, drawings also include crawl space foundation

Interior View - Family Room

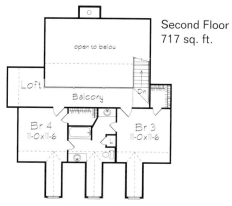

Second Floor
717 sq. ft.

open to below

Loft

Balcony

Dn

Br 4
11-0x11-6

Br 3
11-0x11-6

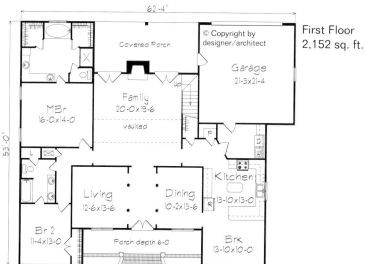

First Floor
2,152 sq. ft.

62'-4"

53'-0"

Covered Porch

© Copyright by designer/architect

Garage
21-3x21-4

Up

MBr
16-0x14-0

Family
20-0x19-6

vaulted

Kitchen
13-10x13-0

Living
12-6x13-6

Dining
10-2x13-6

Br 2
11-4x13-0

Porch depth 6-0

Brk
13-10x10-0

SPECIAL FEATURES

3,793 total square feet of living area

The wide, welcoming foyer showcases columns at the entrance to the great room and dining room

The spacious hearth room, breakfast area and kitchen combine to create a warm, inviting space perfect for cozy nights spent with the family

The optional lower level includes space for a recreation room, bar, bedroom and bath and has an additional 1,588 square feet of living area

3 bedrooms, 2 1/2 baths, 3-car side entry garage

Walk-out basement foundation

Rear View

© Copyright by designer/architect

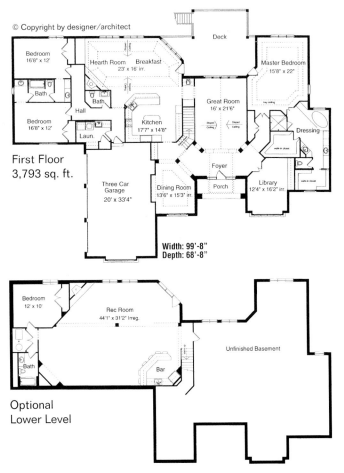

First Floor
3,793 sq. ft.

Bedroom
16'8" x 12'

Bath

Bedroom
16'8" x 12'

Hall

Laun.

Bath

Hearth Room
23' x 16' irr.

Breakfast

Kitchen
17'7" x 14'8"

Deck

Great Room
16' x 21'6"

Master Bedroom
15'8" x 22'

Dressing

Foyer

Library
12'4" x 16'2" irr.

Three Car Garage
20' x 33'4"

Dining Room
13'6" x 15'3" irr.

Porch

Width: 99'-8"
Depth: 68'-8"

Optional
Lower Level

Bedroom
12' x 10'

Rec Room
44'1" x 31'2" Irreg.

Unfinished Basement

Bath

Bar

SPECIAL FEATURES

3,017 total square feet of living area

Convenient L-shaped entry brings formality to this 1 1/2 story plan

The loft features a palladian window overlooking family room

First floor bedrooms each have a private full bath

Master bedroom includes a bay window and corner tub in the bath

Bonus room above the garage is included in the square footage

4 bedrooms, 3 1/2 baths, 2-car side entry garage

Partial basement/crawl space foundation

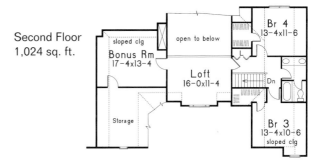

Second Floor
1,024 sq. ft.

sloped clg
Bonus Rm
17-4x13-4
open to below
Br 4
13-4x11-6
Loft
16-0x11-4
Dn
Storage
Br 3
13-4x10-6
sloped clg

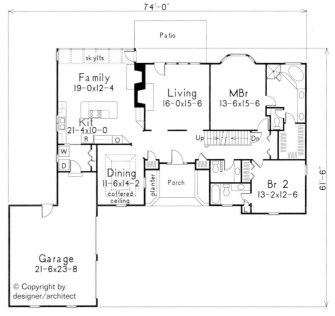

First Floor
1,993 sq. ft.

74'-0"

Patio
skylts
Family
19-0x12-4
Living
16-0x15-6
MBr
13-6x15-6
Kit
21-4x10-0
R O
W
D
Dining
11-6x14-2
coffered ceiling
planter
Porch
Up
Dn
Br 2
13-2x12-6
19'-6"

Garage
21-6x23-8

© Copyright by designer/architect

SPECIAL FEATURES

3,013 total square feet of living area

Oversized rooms throughout

Kitchen features an island sink, large pantry and opens into the breakfast room with a sunroom feel

Large family room with fireplace accesses the rear covered deck and front porch

Master bedroom includes a large walk-in closet and private deluxe bath

4 bedrooms, 3 1/2 baths, 2-car side entry garage

Basement foundation

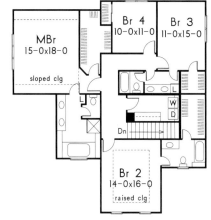

Second Floor
1,554 sq. ft.

MBr
15-0x18-0
sloped clg

Br 4
10-0x11-0

Br 3
11-0x15-0

Br 2
14-0x16-0
raised clg

Dn

W
D

L

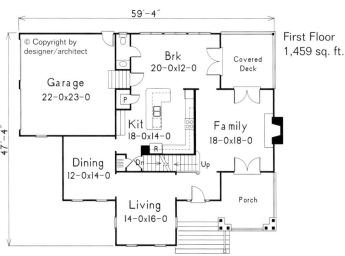

First Floor
1,459 sq. ft.

59'-4"

47'-4"

© Copyright by designer/architect

Garage
22-0x23-0

Brk
20-0x12-0

Covered Deck

Kit
18-0x14-0

Family
18-0x18-0

P

Dining
12-0x14-0

Dn

Up

R

Living
14-0x16-0

Porch

SPECIAL FEATURES

3,117 total square feet of living area

Energy efficient home with
2" x 6" exterior walls

The cheerful kitchen has a
double-bowl sink in the island and
opens up nicely to the dinette area

Spacious two-story great room
offers a pleasant environment for
gathering with family and friends

The relaxing owner's bedroom offers a
bath with a generous closet, double-bowl
vanity, amazing walk-in shower and a
spa-style tub to soak your cares away

3 bedrooms, 2 1/2 baths, 2-car garage

Slab foundation

Second Floor
1,342 sq. ft.

BED RM 2
15 x 14

BED RM 3
16 x 12

OPEN TO
BELOW

BATH

STORAGE
12 x 9

OPEN TO
BELOW

LOFT
14 x 13

BONUS ROOM
GAME 5
21 x 20

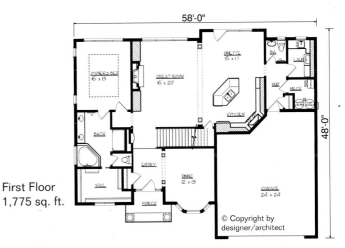

First Floor
1,775 sq. ft.

58'-0"

48'-0"

OWNER'S BED
16 x 13

GREAT ROOM
16 x 20

DINETTE
15 x 11

BA

LAUN

BATH

KITCHEN

MUD

MECH

W.I.C.

ENTRY

DINING
12 x 13

GARAGE
24 x 24

PORCH

© Copyright by
designer/architect

SPECIAL FEATURES

2,618 total square feet of living area

Stylish front facade with covered porch and distinctive window treatment

Great room features a vaulted ceiling, skylights and large fireplace

Master bedroom and bath have two large walk-in closets, separate oversized tub and shower, first floor convenience and privacy

Kitchen overlooks the deck and features circle-top windows and corner window view from the sink

4 bedrooms, 2 1/2 baths, 2-car garage

Basement foundation, drawings also include slab and crawl space foundations

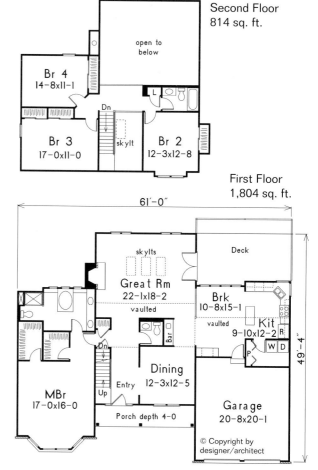

Second Floor
814 sq. ft.

open to below

Br 4
14-8x11-1

Dn

Br 3
17-0x11-0   skylt   Br 2
12-3x12-8

First Floor
1,804 sq. ft.

61'-0"

skylts   Deck

Great Rm
22-1x18-2
vaulted

Brk
10-8x15-1
vaulted

Kit
9-10x12-2

Bar

W D

P

Dn

Dining
12-3x12-5

49'-4"

MBr
17-0x16-0

Up   Entry

Garage
20-8x20-1

Porch depth 4-0

© Copyright by
designer/architect

SPECIAL FEATURES

3,809 total square feet of living area

Entertain guests with a formal dining room, extra-large great room, exciting music room and enchanting rear patio

A first floor master bedroom pampers the homeowner with its luxurious dressing area and large walk-in closet

Three additional bedrooms are located on the second floor and enjoy walk-in closets and private bath access

4 bedrooms, 3 1/2 baths, 3-car side entry garage

Basement foundation

Interior View - Dining Room & Kitchen

Second Floor
1,027 sq. ft.

Bedroom
12'10" x 12'10"

Balcony
10'2" x 6'4"

Bedroom
14'4" x 12'

walk-in closet

Mech.

Bath

Bedroom
17' x 12'

walk-in closet

Sitting Area
8'8" x 11'7"

window seat

Patio
22' x 18'

Dining Room
15'3" x 15'3"
9' ceiling ht.

Kitchen
20' x 15'4"

stairs down

Master Bedroom
14'6" x 15'4"

Pantry

Great Room
21'5" x 27'8"
14' ceiling ht.

9' ceiling ht.

Library
15'6" x 15'2" irr.

walk-in closet

Laun.

Hall
9' ceiling ht.

Foyer
11' ceiling ht.

Music Room
14'9" x 12'2"
11' ceiling ht.

Dressing

walk-in closet

© Copyright by designer/architect

Three Car Garage
21' x 28'9"

Porch

Width: 78'-2"
Depth: 74'-6"

First Floor
2,782 sq. ft.

SPECIAL FEATURES

2,583 total square feet of living area

Triple-gabled entrance with door sidelights

Prominent double bay windows
add dimension and light

Convenient rear stairs

Bonus room above the garage, which is
included in the square footage, converts
to a fifth bedroom or an activity center

Master bedroom has a private bath with a
corner tub surrounded by windows,
walk-in closet and coffered ceiling

4 bedrooms, 2 1/2 baths,
2-car side entry garage

Basement foundation

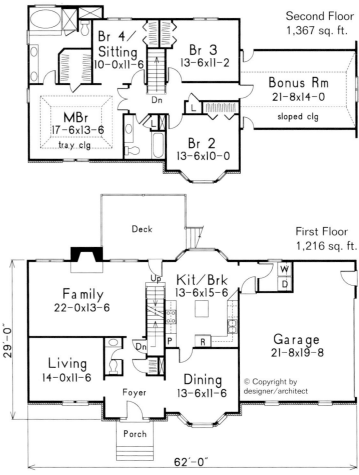

Second Floor
1,367 sq. ft.

Br 4/
Sitting
10-0x11-6

Br 3
13-6x11-2

Bonus Rm
21-8x14-0

sloped clg

MBr
17-6x13-6

tray clg

Dn

Br 2
13-6x10-0

First Floor
1,216 sq. ft.

Deck

Up

Kit/Brk
13-6x15-6

W
D

Family
22-0x13-6

Garage
21-8x19-8

Dn

Living
14-0x11-6

P   R

Dining
13-6x11-6

© Copyright by
designer/architect

Foyer

Porch

29'-0"

62'-0"

SPECIAL FEATURES

3,159 total square feet of living area

An impressive master bath
includes a spacious walk-in closet
and built-in tub perfect for relaxing

The kitchen is open and efficient with a
large, curved island for easy dining

Double-door entry to the study reveals
a beautiful built-in work area and
lovely windows for added light

4 bedrooms, 3 1/2 baths, 3-car garage

Basement foundation

Rear View

Second Floor
1,629 sq. ft.

First Floor
1,530 sq. ft.

© Copyright by
designer/architect

SPECIAL FEATURES

3,664 total square feet of living area

A delightful pub and informal dining area invites family members and guests to relax and enjoy the good times

Decorative columns define the foyer, formal dining room and great room

Boasting a tray ceiling treatment, the master bedroom showcases a bath with a whirlpool tub, double-bowl vanity and large walk-in closet

4 bedrooms, 2 1/2 baths, 3-car side entry garage

Basement foundation

Interior View - Great Room

Second Floor
1,167 sq. ft.

Bedroom
14' x 17'9"

Bedroom
13'9" x 13'6"

Balcony

walk-in closet

Bath

Open to Below

step down

walk-in closet

Bedroom
13'2" x 14'2"

First Floor
2,497 sq. ft.

Patio

Informal Dining
15'2" x 18'6"

Kitchen
14'6" x 14'6"

Pub

Great Room
22'3" x 19'
13' ceiling height

Master Bedroom
17'6" x 13'2"

Laun.

Foyer

walk-in closet

Dining Room
14'6" x 15'6"

Library
11'6" x 15'7"
13' ceiling height

Porch

Three Car Garage
20'8" x 33'5"

65'

© Copyright by designer/architect

74'10"

SPECIAL FEATURES

2,665 total square feet of living area

The fireplace provides a focus for family living by connecting the central living quarters

The abundance of windows, combined with vaulted ceilings, gives this plan a spacious feel

Large sun room opens to the kitchen and breakfast area

Master bedroom features a huge walk-in closet, vaulted ceiling and luxurious bath facilities

Bonus room on the second floor is included in the total square footage

3 bedrooms, 2 1/2 baths, 2-car side entry garage

Crawl space foundation

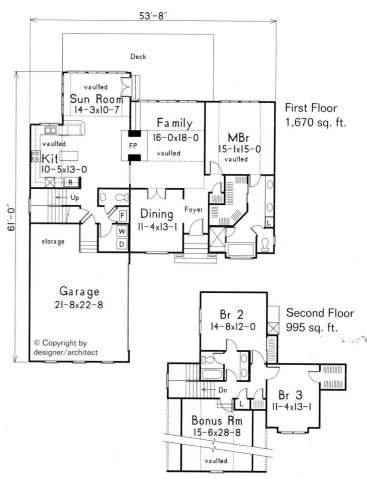

53'-8"

Deck

vaulted

Sun Room
14-3x10-7

Family
16-0x18-0
vaulted

MBr
15-1x15-0
vaulted

First Floor
1,670 sq. ft.

vaulted

Kit
10-5x13-0

R

Up

FP

F
W
D

Dining
11-4x13-1

Foyer

61'-0"

storage

Garage
21-8x22-8

© Copyright by
designer/architect

Br 2
14-8x12-0

Second Floor
995 sq. ft.

Dn

L

Br 3
11-4x13-1

Bonus Rm
15-6x28-8

vaulted

SPECIAL FEATURES

2,715 total square feet of living area

Energy efficient home with
2" x 6" exterior walls

The cheerful kitchen has a double-bowl
sink in the island, a large corner pantry
and opens up to the cheerful dinette area

Double doors off the entry hall lead to
a sophisticated study with access to
the front covered wrap-around porch

The owner's suite has an optional fireplace
and offers a generous closet and a private
bath with a double-bowl vanity, amazing
walk-in shower and a whirlpool tub

4 bedrooms, 2 1/2 baths, 4-car garage

Walk-out basement foundation

Second Floor
1,337 sq. ft.

BED RM 4
10 x 12

OWNER'S SUITE
18 x 15

OPTIONAL FIREPLACE

BATH

WIC

BED RM 3
11 x 12

BATH

LAUN

BED RM 2
12 x 11

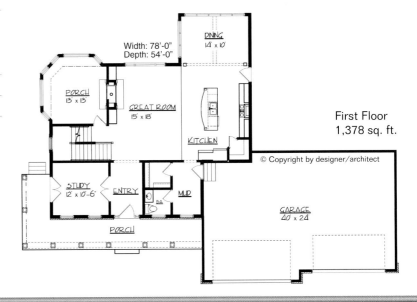

Width: 78'-0"
Depth: 54'-0"

DINING
14 x 10

PORCH
13 x 13

GREAT ROOM
15 x 18

KITCHEN

First Floor
1,378 sq. ft.

© Copyright by designer/architect

STUDY
12 x 10'-6"

ENTRY

BA

MUD

GARAGE
40 x 24

PORCH

SPECIAL FEATURES

2,565 total square feet of living area

Second floor loft adjoins a guest room, private bath and plenty of storage space

Expansive second floor offers privacy with access from the foyer

Complete master bedroom suite has a bay window and a bath with garden tub and walk-in closet

The kitchen is steps away from the bayed breakfast area

3 bedrooms, 3 baths, 2-car garage

Partial basement/crawl space foundation

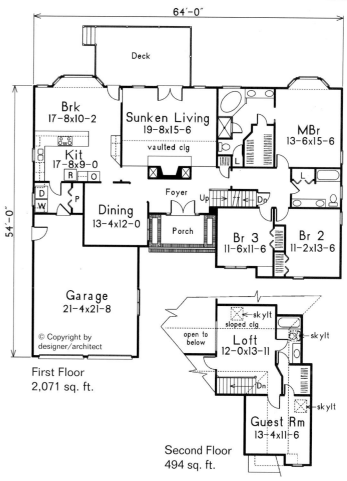

64'-0"

54'-0"

Deck

Brk
17-8x10-2

Sunken Living
19-8x15-6
vaulted clg

MBr
13-6x15-6

Kit
17-8x9-0

Foyer

Up

Dn

Dining
13-4x12-0

Porch

Br 3
11-6x11-6

Br 2
11-2x13-6

Garage
21-4x21-8

© Copyright by designer/architect

First Floor
2,071 sq. ft.

skylt
sloped clg

open to below

Loft
12-0x13-11

skylt

Dn

skylt

Guest Rm
13-4x11-6

Second Floor
494 sq. ft.

SPECIAL FEATURES

3,688 total square feet of living area

Formal and informal spaces provide for various social events and comfortable family living

A gourmet kitchen with open bar and island serves the dining room and breakfast area with equal ease

A secluded hall creates an orderly transition from the kitchen to the laundry room and garage

A wonderful master bedroom is decorated by a stepped ceiling, crown molding, boxed window and lavish bath with a platform whirlpool tub

4 bedrooms, 3 1/2 baths, 3-car side entry garage

Basement foundation

Rear View

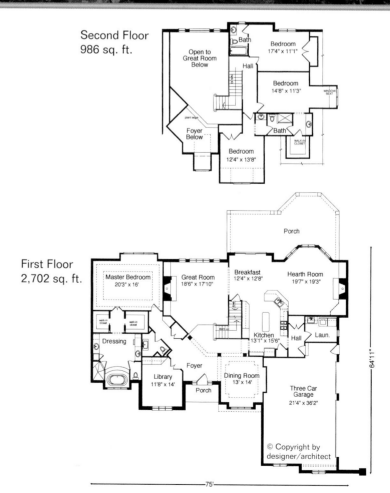

Second Floor
986 sq. ft.

Open to Great Room Below

Bath

Bedroom
17'4" x 11'1"

Hall

Bedroom
14'8" x 11'3"

WINDOW SEAT

Foyer Below

plant ledge

Bath

WALK-IN CLOSET

Bedroom
12'4" x 13'8"

First Floor
2,702 sq. ft.

Porch

Master Bedroom
20'3" x 16'

Great Room
18'6" x 17'10"

Breakfast
12'4" x 12'8"

Hearth Room
19'7" x 19'3"

walk in closet

walk in closet

Kitchen
13'1" x 15'6"

Hall

Laun.

Dressing

Library
11'8" x 14'

Foyer

Dining Room
13' x 14'

Three Car Garage
21'4" x 36'2"

Porch

64'1"

75'

SPECIAL FEATURES

2,463 total square feet of living area

Exciting angular design
with diagonal stairway

Living room features a vaulted ceiling,
fireplace and convenient wet bar

Generously sized family room
features a vaulted ceiling and
easy access to the kitchen

Sunny bay window defines the breakfast
area that accesses the deck

4 bedrooms, 2 1/2 baths, 2-car garage

Basement foundation

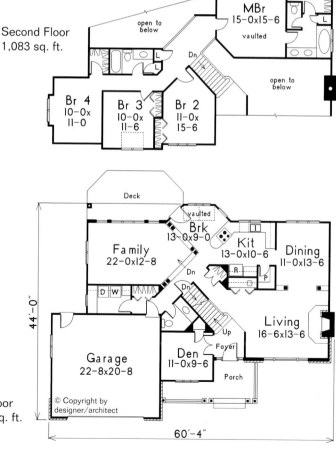

Second Floor
1,083 sq. ft.

MBr
15-0x15-6
vaulted

open to
below

Dn

open to
below

Br 4
10-0x
11-0

Br 3
10-0x
11-6

Br 2
11-0x
15-6

Deck

vaulted

Brk
13-0x9-0

Kit
13-0x10-6

Dining
11-0x13-6

Family
22-0x12-8

Dn

R

P

Dn

Living
16-6x13-6

D W

Up

Garage
22-8x20-8

Den
11-0x9-6

Foyer

Porch

© Copyright by
designer/architect

First Floor
1,380 sq. ft.

44'-0"

60'-4"

SPECIAL FEATURES

3,368 total square feet of living area

Sunken great room features a cathedral ceiling, wooden beams, skylights and a masonry fireplace

Octagon-shaped breakfast room has domed ceiling with beams, large windows and door to patio

Private master bedroom has a deluxe bath and dressing area

Oversized walk-in closets and storage areas are located in each bedroom

4 bedrooms, 3 full baths, 2 half baths, 2-car side entry garage

Basement foundation

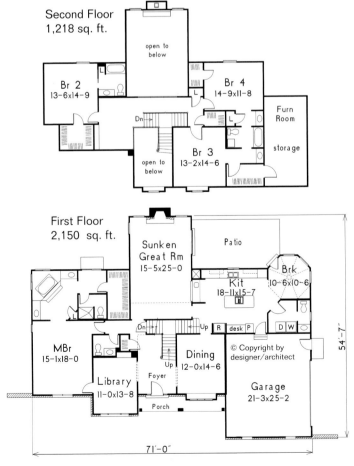

Second Floor
1,218 sq. ft.

open to below

Br 2
13-6x14-9

Br 4
14-9x11-8

Furn Room

storage

Dn

Br 3
13-2x14-6

open to below

First Floor
2,150 sq. ft.

Sunken Great Rm
15-5x25-0

Patio

Brk
10-6x10-6

Kit
18-11x15-7

Dn   Up   R   desk   P   D   W

© Copyright by designer/architect

MBr
15-1x18-0

Dining
12-0x14-6

Up

Garage
21-3x25-2

Library
11-0x13-8

Foyer

Porch

54'-7"

71'-0"

SPECIAL FEATURES

3,109 total square feet of living area

Energy efficient home with
2" x 6" exterior walls

The elegant entry leads into the quiet
great room that is perfect for relaxing
with family or partying with friends

The stunning kitchen features a walk-in
pantry, snack bar island and opens to the
casual nook and formal dining room

A lovely three-season porch allows you to
enjoy the great outdoors in any weather

4 bedrooms, 2 1/2 baths,
3-car side entry garage

Walk-out basement foundation

Interior View - Great Room

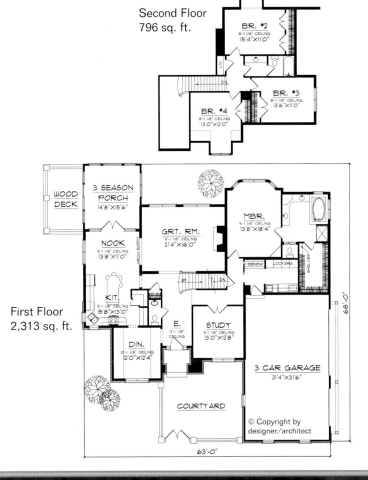

Second Floor
796 sq. ft.

BR. #2
8'-1 1/8" CEILING
15'4"x11'0"

BR. #3
8'-1 1/8" CEILING
13'6"x11'0"

BR. #4
8'-1 1/8" CEILING
13'0"x12'0"

First Floor
2,313 sq. ft.

WOOD DECK

3 SEASON PORCH
14'8"x15'6"

NOOK
9'-1 1/8" CEILING
13'8"x11'0"

GRT. RM.
12'-1 1/8" CEILING
21'4"x16'0"

MBR.
9'-1 1/8" CEILING
13'8"x18'4"

KIT.
9'-1 1/8" CEILING
15'8"x13'0"

DIN.
10'-1 1/8" CEILING
12'0"x12'4"

E.
12'-1 1/8" CEILING

STUDY
9'-1 1/8" CEILING
13'0"x12'8"

3 CAR GARAGE
21'4"x31'6"

COURTYARD

© Copyright by
designer/architect

63'-0"

68'-0"

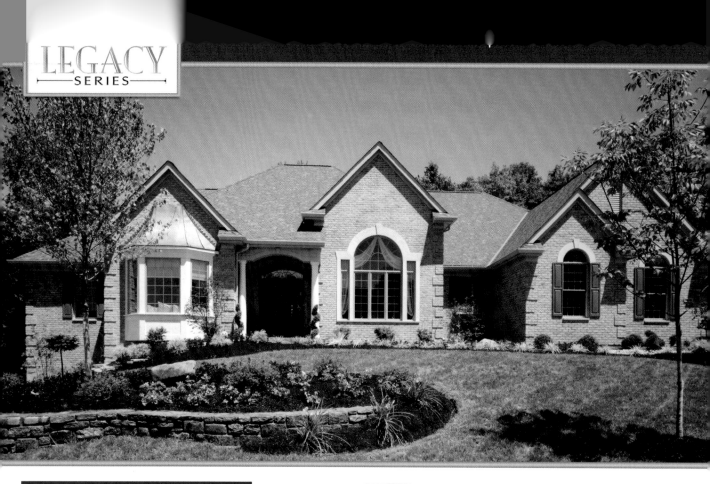

LEGACY
SERIES

SPECIAL FEATURES

3,421 total square feet of living area

The gourmet kitchen with island and snack bar combines with the spacious breakfast and hearth rooms to create a warm and friendly atmosphere

The luxurious master bedroom with sitting area and fireplace is complemented by a deluxe bath designed to pamper

The optional lower level has an additional 1,777 square feet of living area and offers fun and excitement

3 bedrooms, 3 1/2 baths, 4-car side entry garage

Walk-out basement foundation

Interior View - Great Room

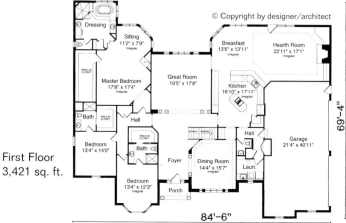

© Copyright by designer/architect

First Floor
3,421 sq. ft.

- Dressing
- Sitting 11'2" x 7'9" Irregular
- WALK IN CLOSET
- Master Bedroom 17'8" x 17'4" Irregular
- Great Room 19'5" x 17'8"
- Breakfast 13'6" x 13'11" Irregular
- Hearth Room 22'11" x 17'1" Irregular
- Kitchen 16'10" x 17'11" Irregular
- Bath
- WALK IN CLOSET
- Hall
- Bedroom 13'4" x 14'0"
- WALK IN CLOSET
- Bath
- Foyer
- Dining Room 14'4" x 15'7" Irregular
- Hall
- Laun.
- Garage 21'4" x 40'11"
- Bedroom 13'4" x 12'3" Irregular
- Porch

69'-4"

84'-6"

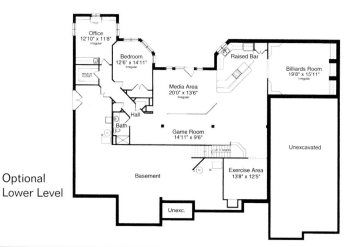

Optional
Lower Level

- Office 12'10" x 11'8" Irregular
- Bedroom 12'6" x 14'11" Irregular
- WALK IN CLOSET
- Raised Bar
- Billiards Room 19'8" x 15'11" Irregular
- Media Area 20'0" x 13'6" Irregular
- Bath
- Hall
- Game Room 14'11" x 9'6"
- Basement
- Exercise Area 13'8" x 12'5"
- Unexcavated
- Unex.

SPECIAL FEATURES

2,773 total square feet of living area

Extensive use of bay and other large windows front and rear adds brightness and space

Master bedroom suite features double-door entrance, oversized walk-in closet and tray ceiling

Rear stairway leads to both the bonus room, which is included in the square footage, and the laundry area on the second floor

4 bedrooms, 2 1/2 baths, 2-car side entry garage

Basement foundation

Interior View - Family Room

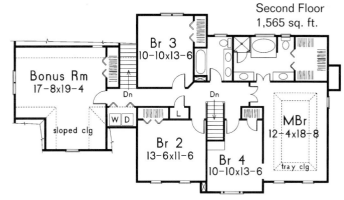

Second Floor
1,565 sq. ft.

Bonus Rm 17-8x19-4

sloped clg

Br 3 10-10x13-6

Br 2 13-6x11-6

Br 4 10-10x13-6

MBr 12-4x18-8
tray clg

Dn   Dn   W D   L

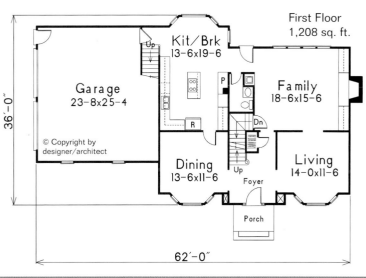

First Floor
1,208 sq. ft.

Garage 23-8x25-4

Kit/Brk 13-6x19-6

Family 18-6x15-6

Dining 13-6x11-6

Living 14-0x11-6

Foyer

Porch

Up   Dn   Up   P   R

© Copyright by designer/architect

36'-0"

62'-0"

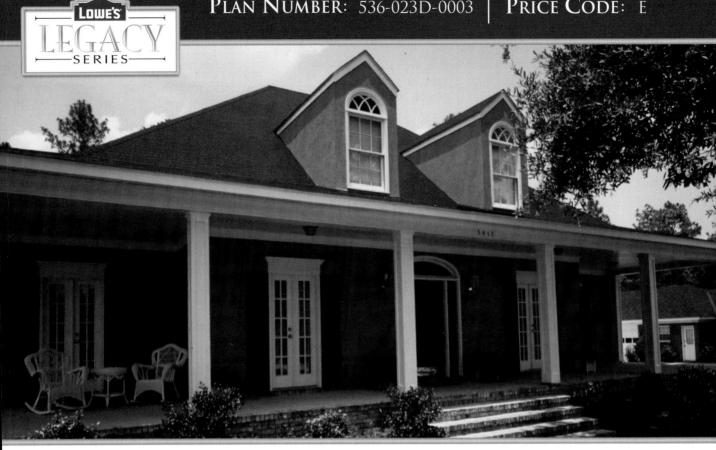

SPECIAL FEATURES

2,824 total square feet of living area

9' ceilings on the first floor

Second floor bedrooms feature private dressing areas and share a bath

Large great room includes a fireplace flanked by French doors leading to the rear patio

Kitchen conveniently serves the formal dining room and breakfast area that features a large bay window

4 bedrooms, 3 baths, 2-car side entry garage

Slab foundation, drawings also include crawl space foundation

Rear View

Second Floor
704 sq. ft.

Br 2
12-10x15-5

Dn

Br 3
11-6x15-5

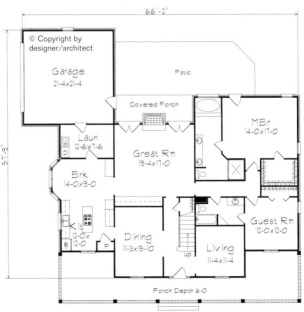

66'-2"

© Copyright by designer/architect

Garage
21-4x21-4

Patio

Covered Porch

Laun
12-6x7-6

Great Rm
19-4x17-0

MBr
14-0x17-0

First Floor
2,120 sq. ft.

Brk
14-0x9-0

57'-9"

Kit
12-0x
12-0

Dining
11-3x15-10

Living
11-4x11-4

Guest Rm
12-0x12-0

Up

Porch Depth 6-0

SPECIAL FEATURES

3,816 total square feet of living area

Beautifully designed master bedroom enjoys a lavish dressing area as well as access to the library

Second floor computer loft is centrally located and includes plenty of counterspace

The two-story great room has an impressive arched opening and a beautiful beamed ceiling

The outdoor covered deck has a popular fireplace

4 bedrooms, 3 1/2 baths, 3-car side entry garage

Basement foundation

Interior View - Great Room

Second Floor
1,091 sq. ft.

First Floor
2,725 sq. ft.

© Copyright by designer/architect

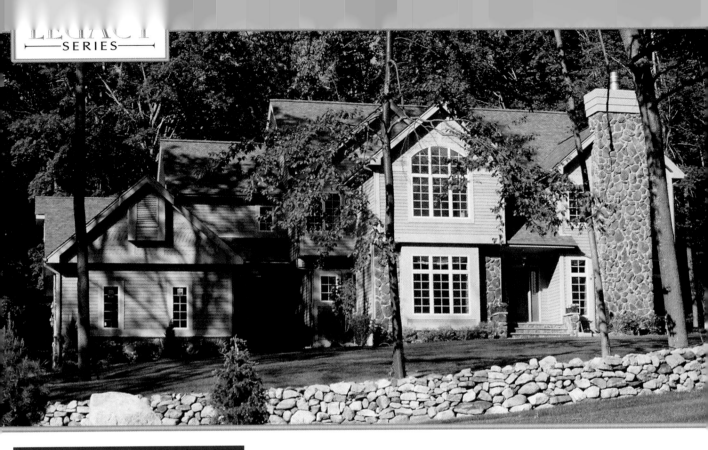

LEGACY SERIES

SPECIAL FEATURES

3,107 total square feet of living area

The cozy living room has a fireplace centered between two windows for added light

Step down from the kitchen and breakfast room into a spacious and comfortable family room

All the bedrooms are located on the second floor for convenience to one another and privacy from the main living areas

4 bedrooms, 2 1/2 baths, 3-car side entry garage

Basement foundation

Second Floor
1,468 sq. ft.

First Floor
1,639 sq. ft.

SPECIAL FEATURES

2,525 total square feet of living area

Energy efficient home with
2" x 6" exterior walls

The cheerful kitchen has
a double-bowl sink in the island,
a large corner pantry and opens up
nicely to the dinette area and sunroom

Double doors off the entry hall
lead to a sophisticated study with
plenty of peace and quiet

The owner's suite is topped with a coffered
ceiling and offers a generous closet and
a private bath with a double-bowl vanity,
amazing walk-in shower and a whirlpool tub

4 bedrooms, 2 1/2 baths, 3-car garage

Walk-out basement foundation

Second Floor
1,280 sq. ft.

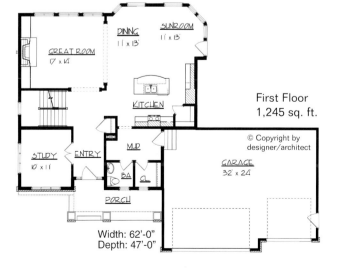

First Floor
1,245 sq. ft.

© Copyright by
designer/architect

Width: 62'-0"
Depth: 47'-0"

LEGACY SERIES

SPECIAL FEATURES

2,461 total square feet of living area

The cooktop island in the kitchen has ample counterspace for easy food preparation and connects to the cozy hearth room

Luxurious master suite has a large closet with conveniently separated hanging areas

The covered deck/screened porch with vaulted ceiling creates a great outdoor gathering area

The optional second floor has an additional 518 square feet of living area

3 bedrooms, 3 1/2 baths, 3-car side entry garage

Basement foundation

Interior View - Kitchen

First Floor
2,461 sq. ft.

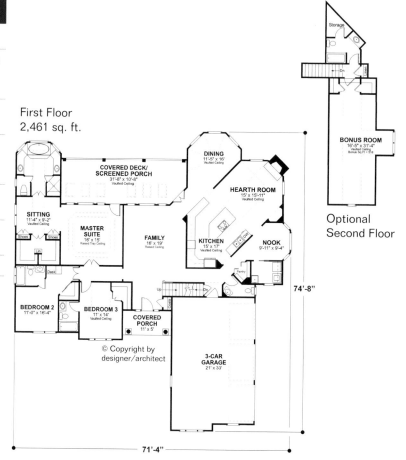

Optional
Second Floor

BONUS ROOM
16'-5" x 31'-4"
Vaulted Ceiling
Bonus Sq Ft = 518

Storage

DINING
11'-5" x 16'
Vaulted Ceiling

HEARTH ROOM
15' x 15'-11"
Vaulted Ceiling

COVERED DECK/
SCREENED PORCH
31'-8" x 10'-8"
Vaulted Ceiling

SITTING
11'-4" x 9'-2"
Vaulted Ceiling

MASTER
SUITE
16' x 15'
Raised Tray Ceiling

FAMILY
16' x 19'
Raised Ceiling

KITCHEN
15' x 17'
Vaulted Ceiling

NOOK
9'-11" x 9'-4"

BEDROOM 2
11'-0" x 16'-4"

BEDROOM 3
11' x 14'
Vaulted Ceiling

COVERED
PORCH
11' x 5'

3-CAR
GARAGE
21' x 33'

© Copyright by
designer/architect

74'-8"

71'-4"

SERIES

SPECIAL FEATURES

3,265 total square feet of living area

Double doors off the main hallway lead into a private study with a 9' ceiling

Two storage spaces are easily accessible when storing household items

The master bedroom has its own plush luxury bath and walk-in closet

4 bedrooms, 2 1/2 baths, 2-car side entry garage

Basement foundation

Interior View - Study

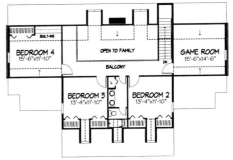

Second Floor
1,248 sq. ft.

First Floor
2,017 sq. ft.

© Copyright by
designer/architect

SPECIAL FEATURES

2,895 total square feet of living area

Ornate triple-arched window across entire end of master bedroom is a beautiful focal point

Substantial bonus room available above garage is included in the square footage

Solid step-up covered entrance

Convenient open breakfast area is near a peninsula counter and has easy access to the laundry room and rear deck

4 bedrooms, 2 1/2 baths, 2-car side entry garage

Basement foundation

Second Floor
1,605 sq. ft.

Bonus Rm
20-1x13-5
sloped clg

Br 4
9-11x13-9

Dn

L

Dn

Br 2
12-8x14-5

MBr
12-6x17-8

Br 3
13-6x11-6

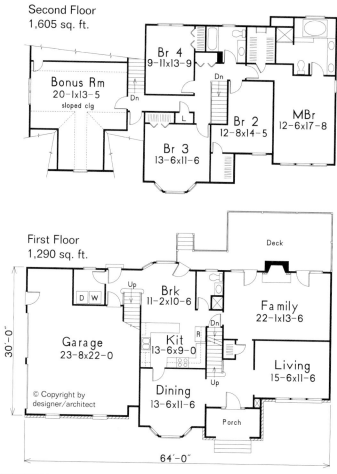

First Floor
1,290 sq. ft.

Deck

Up

Brk
11-2x10-6

Family
22-1x13-6

D W

Garage
23-8x22-0

Kit
13-6x9-0

R

Dn

Living
15-6x11-6

Up

30'-0"

Dining
13-6x11-6

Porch

© Copyright by
designer/architect

64'-0"

SPECIAL FEATURES

4,652 total square feet of living area

A grand foyer introduces a formal dining room and library with beamed ceiling and built-ins

Covered porches at the rear of the home offer splendid views

A magnificent master bedroom has a 10' ceiling, a private sitting area and a luxurious dressing room with walk-in closet

Secondary bedrooms have window seats, large closets and private bath access

4 bedrooms, 3 1/2 baths, 3-car side entry garage

Walk-out basement foundation

Interior View - Great Room

Second Floor
1,238 sq. ft.

First Floor
3,414 sq. ft.

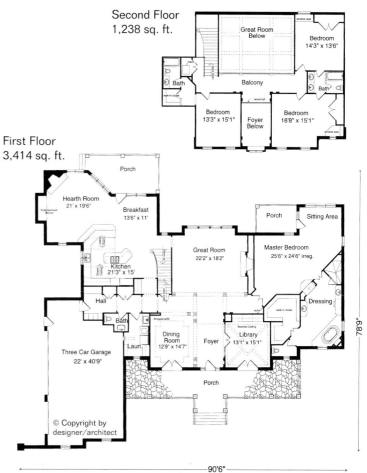

© Copyright by designer/architect

SPECIAL FEATURES

3,216 total square feet of living area

All bedrooms include private full baths

Hearth room, breakfast area and kitchen create a large informal gathering area

Oversized family room boasts a fireplace, wet bar and bay window

Master bedroom has two walk-in closets and a luxurious bath

4 bedrooms, 4 1/2 baths, 3-car side entry garage

Walk-out basement foundation

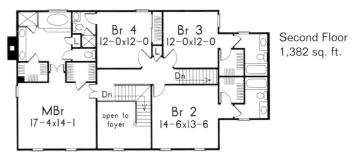

Second Floor
1,382 sq. ft.

Br 4
12-0x12-0

Br 3
12-0x12-0

MBr
17-4x14-1

open to foyer

Br 2
14-6x13-6

Dn

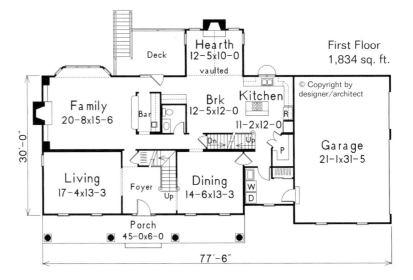

First Floor
1,834 sq. ft.

Deck

Hearth
12-5x10-0
vaulted

Family
20-8x15-6

Bar

Brk
12-5x12-0

Kitchen

R

© Copyright by
designer/architect

Garage
21-1x31-5

P

Living
17-4x13-3

Foyer

Dining
14-6x13-3

W
D

Up

Dn

Up

30'-0"

Porch
45-0x6-0

77'-6"

SPECIAL FEATURES

3,445 total square feet of living area

The flow of the first floor enhances the enjoyment of entertaining guests in the formal living and dining rooms, while the kitchen, hearth room and breakfast area combine for a comfortable atmosphere

Double pocket doors close off the hearth room from the formal dining room when entertaining

The rear deck has a beautiful gazebo attached for added outdoor living space

4 bedrooms, 3 1/2 baths, 3-car side entry garage

Walk-out basement foundation, drawings also include crawl space foundation

Interior View - Dining Room

Second Floor
1,779 sq. ft.

Bedroom
13'7" x 17'1"
8' ceiling height

Master Bedroom
16'11" x 20'8"
9' ceiling height

Dressing

Dressing

walk-in closet

laundry chute

Hall

linen

Bedroom
16'10" x 12'9"
8' ceiling height

walk-in closet

stairs dn 4 risers

walk-in closet

Bath

Balcony

Bedroom
15'10" x 12'0"
9' ceiling height

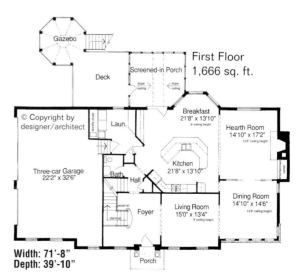

Gazebo

Deck

Screened-in Porch
slope ceiling   slope ceiling

First Floor
1,666 sq. ft.

© Copyright by designer/architect

laundry chute

Laun.

Breakfast
21'8" x 13'10"
9' ceiling height

Hearth Room
14'10" x 17'2"
12'8" ceiling height

Three-car Garage
22'2" x 32'6"

Kitchen
21'8" x 13'10"

Bath

Hall

Dining Room
14'10" x 14'6"
12'8" ceiling height

wood rail stairs up

Foyer

Living Room
15'0" x 13'4"
9' ceiling height

Width: 71'-8"
Depth: 39'-10"

Porch

SPECIAL FEATURES

1,859 total square feet of living area

Fireplace highlights the vaulted great room

Master bedroom includes
a large closet and private bath

The kitchen adjoins the breakfast room
providing easy access to the outdoors

3 bedrooms, 2 1/2 baths, 2-car garage

Basement foundation

Second Floor
789 sq. ft.

Br 2
10-8x11-3

MBr
11-10x17-2

Dn

Br 3
11-8x10-2

open to
below

First Floor
1,070 sq. ft.

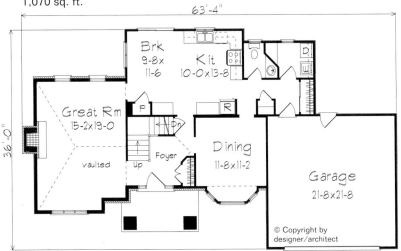

63'-4"

36'-0"

Brk
9-8x
11-6

Kit
10-0x13-8

Great Rm
15-2x19-0

Dn

vaulted

Foyer

Up

P

R

Dining
11-8x11-2

Garage
21-8x21-8

SPECIAL FEATURES

2,157 total square feet of living area

Varied ceiling treatments, spacious rooms and lots of windows combine to set this home apart from the ordinary

A spacious kitchen has a peninsula and walk-in pantry

The master bedroom has every luxury imagined

4 bedrooms, 2 1/2 baths, 2-car side entry garage

Walk-out basement foundation

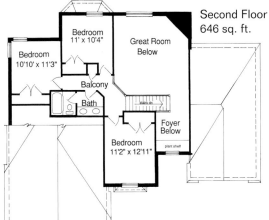

Second Floor
646 sq. ft.

Bedroom
11' x 10'4"

Bedroom
10'10' x 11'3"

Great Room
Below

Balcony

Bath

stairs dn

Foyer
Below

plant shelf

Bedroom
11'2" x 12'11"

Interior View - Great Room

Deck

Breakfast
11' x 9'

Great Room
16'6" x 17'2"

Master
Bedroom
14' x 17'10"

slope ceiling   slope ceiling

Hall

Kitchen
13'2" x 12'7"

Laun.

pantry   wood rail   stairs up
stairs dn

walk-in closet

Two-car Garage
23'9" x 20'0"

Dining Room
11'2" x 15'4"

Foyer

Bath

© Copyright by
designer/architect

First Floor
1,511 sq. ft.

54'8"

46'8"

Special Features

2,358 total square feet of living area

The U-shaped kitchen provides an ideal layout; adjoining breakfast room allows for casual dining

Formal dining and living rooms have attractive floor-to-ceiling windows

Master bedroom includes a deluxe bath

4 bedrooms, 2 1/2 baths, 2-car garage

Basement foundation, drawings also include crawl space and slab foundations

Second Floor
1,140 sq. ft.

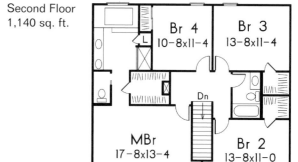

Br 4
10-8x11-4

Br 3
13-8x11-4

Dn

MBr
17-8x13-4

Br 2
13-8x11-0

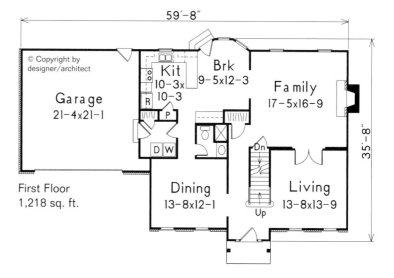

59′-8″

© Copyright by designer/architect

Garage
21-4x21-1

Kit
10-3x10-3

R

P

D W

Brk
9-5x12-3

Family
17-5x16-9

35′-8″

Dn

First Floor
1,218 sq. ft.

Dining
13-8x12-1

Up

Living
13-8x13-9

SPECIAL FEATURES

4,517 total square feet of living area

A brick and stone exterior with a striking turret creates a strong facade for this delightful home

An extra-large hearth room with gas fireplace connects to the breakfast area and kitchen for a comfortable family gathering place

The spectacular lower level features a large recreation room, wine room, exercise room with sauna and two additional bedrooms

3 bedrooms, 2 full baths, 2 half baths, 3-car side entry garage

Walk-out basement foundation

First Floor
2,562 sq. ft.

Width: 75'-8"
Depth: 70'-6"

© Copyright by designer/architect

Rear View

Lower Level
1,955 sq. ft.

SPECIAL FEATURES

2,262 total square feet of living area

Energy efficient home with
2" x 6" exterior walls

Charming exterior features include
large front porch, two patios, front
balcony and double bay windows

The den provides an impressive
entry to the sunken family room

Large master bedroom has a
walk-in closet, dressing area and bath

3 bedrooms, 2 1/2 baths,
2-car rear entry garage

Crawl space foundation, drawings also
include basement and slab foundations

Rear View

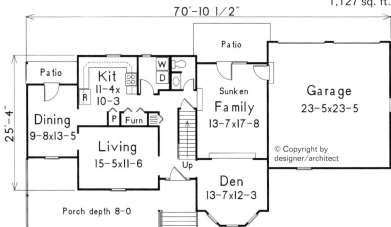

Second Floor
1,135 sq. ft.

Br 2
15-2x11-3

Dn

MBr
13-7x22-9

Br 3
15-5x10-10

Balcony

First Floor
1,127 sq. ft.

70'-10 1/2"

Patio

25'-4"

Patio

Kit
11-4x
10-3

W D

Sunken
Family
13-7x17-8

Garage
23-5x23-5

Dining
9-8x13-5

P Furn

Living
15-5x11-6

Up

© Copyright by
designer/architect

Den
13-7x12-3

Porch depth 8-0

SPECIAL FEATURES

2,396 total square feet of living area

A wall of glass partially separates the sun room from the breakfast room providing a cheerful atmosphere in both of these spaces

The kitchen is filled with function including a large center island, a home office space, and baking and recycling centers

A unique "swing suite" has direct access to a full bath and a convenient first floor location

4 bedrooms, 3 1/2 baths, 3-car garage

Basement foundation

Interior View - Sun Room

Second Floor
1,158 sq. ft.

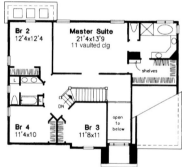

Br 2
12'4x12'4

Master Suite
21'4x13'9
11 vaulted clg

shelves

Br 4
11'4x10

Br 3
11'8x11

open to below

DN

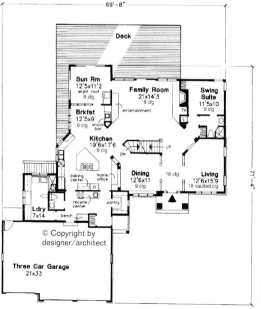

69'-8"

71'-4"

Deck

Sun Rm
12'5x11'2
skylit roof
9 clg

Family Room
21x14'3
9 clg

Swing Suite
11'5x10
9 clg

Brkfst
12'5x9
9 clg

snack bar

entertainment

TV

Kitchen
19'6x17'6
9 clg

UP

DN

baking center

home office

Dining
12'6x11
9 clg

18 clg

Living
12'6x15'9
18 vaulted clg

recycle center

pantry

Ldry
7x14

bench

© Copyright by
designer/architect

Three Car Garage
21x33

First Floor
1,238 sq. ft.

SPECIAL FEATURES

2,614 total square feet of living area

Grand two-story entry features a majestic palladian window, double French doors to the parlor and access to the powder room

State-of-the-art kitchen has corner sink with two large archtop windows, island snack bar, menu desk and walk-in pantry

Master bath is vaulted and offers a luxurious step-up tub, palladian window, built-in shelves and columns with plant shelf

4 bedrooms, 2 1/2 baths, 2-car garage

Basement foundation

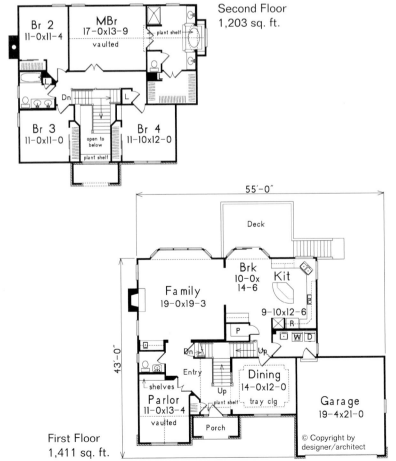

Second Floor
1,203 sq. ft.

Br 2
11-0x11-4

MBr
17-0x13-9
vaulted

plant shelf

Dn   L

Br 3
11-0x11-0

open to below

plant shelf

Br 4
11-10x12-0

55'-0"

Deck

Brk
10-0x14-6

Kit
9-10x12-6

R

W D

Family
19-0x19-3

43'-0"

P

Dn   Up

Entry

shelves

Up

Dining
14-0x12-0
tray clg

plant shelf

Parlor
11-0x13-4
vaulted

Porch

Garage
19-4x21-0

© Copyright by designer/architect

First Floor
1,411 sq. ft.

SPECIAL FEATURES

3,172 total square feet of living area

Energy efficient home with
2" x 6" exterior walls

The master bedroom is a luxurious retreat
with two walk-in closets and a deluxe bath
including a whirlpool tub in a bay window

The kitchen features a cooktop island
with eating bar and opens to the nook
with access onto the rear porch

Bedrooms #2 and #3 each feature a cozy
window seat and share a Jack and Jill bath

4 bedrooms, 3 1/2 baths,
3-car side entry garage

Basement foundation

Second Floor
1,063 sq. ft.

First Floor
2,109 sq. ft.

© Copyright by
designer/architect

SPECIAL FEATURES

2,336 total square feet of living area

Two-story foyer with large second floor window creates a sunny, spacious entrance area

Second floor play room is conveniently located near bedrooms as well as the laundry room

Master bath has a vaulted ceiling and luxurious appointments

Coffered ceiling enhances the master bedroom

4 bedrooms, 2 1/2 baths, 2-car garage

Basement foundation

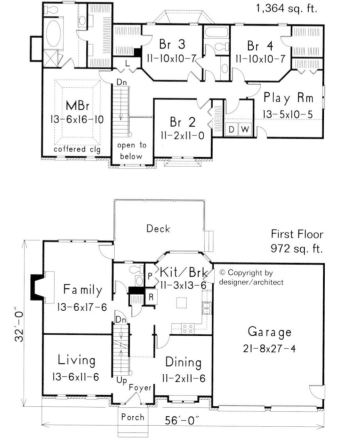

Second Floor
1,364 sq. ft.

Br 3
11-10x10-7

Br 4
11-10x10-7

MBr
13-6x16-10

coffered clg

Dn

open to below

Br 2
11-2x11-0

D W

Play Rm
13-5x10-5

First Floor
972 sq. ft.

Deck

Family
13-6x17-6

Kit/Brk
11-3x13-6

© Copyright by designer/architect

P

R

Dn

Garage
21-8x27-4

Living
13-6x11-6

Dining
11-2x11-6

Up
Foyer

Porch

32'-0"

56'-0"

SPECIAL FEATURES

3,320 total square feet of living area

Energy efficient home with
2" x 6" exterior walls

The sunny octagon-shaped dining
room has access to the rear deck

The double-sided fireplace warms the great
room and the hearth room providing a bold
statement that homeowners will enjoy

The lower level boasts a corner
fireplace in the expansive family
room and access to a large storage
area, which is highly convenient

3 bedrooms, 2 1/2 baths, 3-car garage

Walk-out basement foundation

Interior View - Great Room

DECK

69'-0"

DINING
10'-4"x10'-10"
9'-0" CLG

HEARTH RM
13'-0"x11'-0"
9'-0" CLG

GREAT RM
15'-0"x16'-0"
18'-0" VAULTED CLG

MASTER
BEDROOM
12'-0"x17'-0"
9'-0" CLG

BATH

KITCHEN
13'-0"x13'-4"

PANT

ENTRY
7'-0"x9'-0"
18'-0" VAULTED CLG

WIC

LAUN

PORCH

STUDY
13'-0"x13'-8"
9'-0" CLG

UP

© Copyright by
designer/architect

56'-0"

3 CAR GARAGE
31'-4"x23'-8"

First Floor
1,920 sq. ft.

BED RM
12'-4"x11'-8"
8'-0" CLG

BED RM
11'-4"x14'-6"
8'-0" CLG

FAMILY ROOM
18'-10"x24'-6"
8'-0" CLG

GAME
ROOM
14'8"x19'-4"
8'-0" CLG

HALL

WET BAR

UP

Lower Level
1,400 sq. ft.

UTILITY
24'-0"x9'-0"

STORAGE

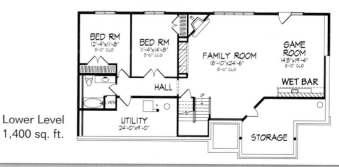

SPECIAL FEATURES

2,223 total square feet of living area

Vaulted master bedroom opens
to a private courtyard

Master bath features a curved glass
block wall around the tub and shower

Vaulted family room combines with
the breakfast room and kitchen to
create a large casual living area

Second floor includes secondary
bedrooms and a possible loft/office

3 bedrooms, 2 1/2 baths, 2-car garage

Basement foundation

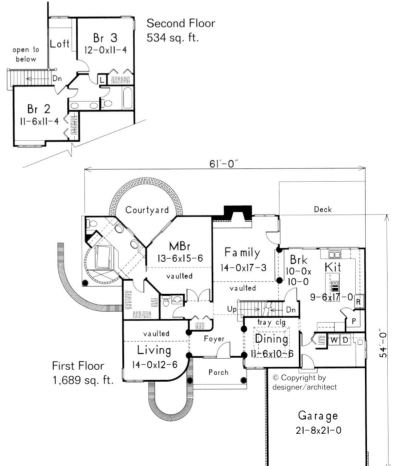

Second Floor
534 sq. ft.

open to below

Loft

Br 3
12-0x11-4

Dn

Br 2
11-6x11-4

First Floor
1,689 sq. ft.

61'-0"

Courtyard

Deck

MBr
13-6x15-6
vaulted

Family
14-0x17-3
vaulted

Brk
10-0x
10-0

Kit
9-6x17-0

Up   Dn

tray clg

vaulted

Living
14-0x12-6

Foyer

Dining
11-6x10-6

Porch

© Copyright by
designer/architect

54'-0"

W D

Garage
21-8x21-0

SPECIAL FEATURES

2,282 total square feet of living area

Balcony and two-story foyer add spaciousness to this compact plan

First floor master bedroom has a corner tub in the large private bath

Out-of-the-way kitchen is open to the full-windowed breakfast room

4 bedrooms, 2 1/2 baths, 2-car drive under side entry garage

Basement foundation

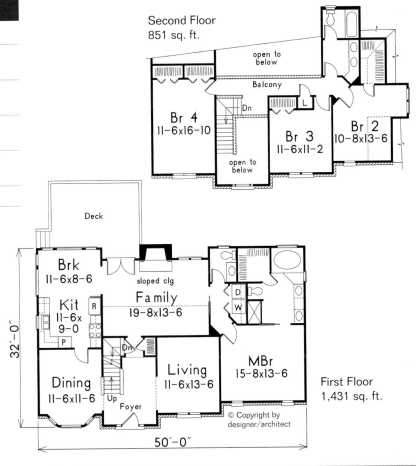

Second Floor
851 sq. ft.

open to below

Balcony

Br 4
11-6x16-10

Dn

L

Br 3
11-6x11-2

Br 2
10-8x13-6

open to below

Deck

Brk
11-6x8-6

sloped clg

Kit
11-6x
9-0

R

Family
19-8x13-6

D

W

Dining
11-6x11-6

Dn

Up

Foyer

Living
11-6x13-6

MBr
15-8x13-6

First Floor
1,431 sq. ft.

32'-0"

50'-0"

© Copyright by designer/architect

SPECIAL FEATURES

2,411 total square feet of living area

Elegant entrance features a
two-story vaulted foyer

Large family room is enhanced by a
masonry fireplace and wet bar

Master bath includes a walk-in closet,
oversized tub and separate shower

Second floor study could easily
convert to a fourth bedroom

3 bedrooms, 2 1/2 baths, 2-car garage

Basement foundation, drawings also
include slab and crawl space foundations

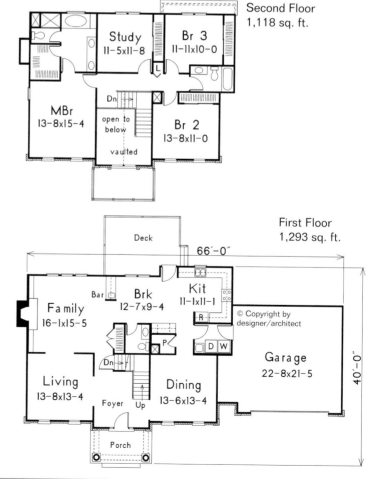

Second Floor
1,118 sq. ft.

Study
11-5x11-8

Br 3
11-11x10-0

MBr
13-8x15-4

Dn

open to
below

Br 2
13-8x11-0

vaulted

First Floor
1,293 sq. ft.

Deck

66'-0"

Bar

Brk
12-7x9-4

Kit
11-1x11-1

Family
16-1x15-5

R

© Copyright by
designer/architect

Dn

P

D W

Garage
22-8x21-5

40'-0"

Living
13-8x13-4

Dining
13-6x13-4

Foyer

Up

Porch

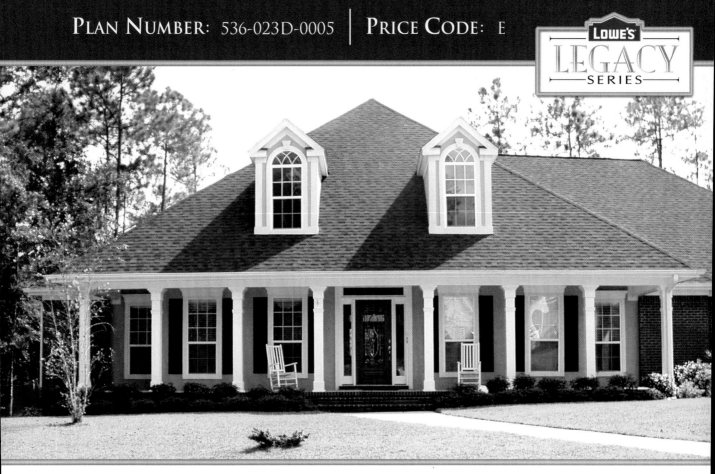

SPECIAL FEATURES

2,672 total square feet of living area

9' ceilings on the first floor

Combined kitchen and breakfast area

Large family room is graced
by a corner fireplace

Convenient storage above garage

Rear covered porch is adjacent to
bedroom #2 and the family room

Future room on the second floor has an
additional 161 square feet of living area

4 bedrooms, 3 baths, 2-car rear entry garage

Slab foundation, drawings also
include crawl space foundation

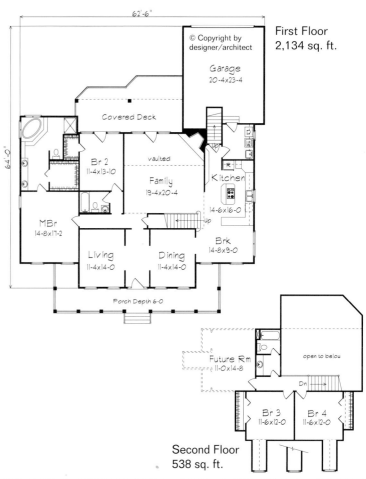

First Floor
2,134 sq. ft.

© Copyright by
designer/architect

Garage
20-4x23-4

Covered Deck

Br 2
11-4x13-10

vaulted

Family
19-4x20-4

Kitchen
14-6x16-0

MBr
14-8x17-2

Brk
14-8x9-0

Living
11-4x14-0

Dining
11-4x14-0

Porch Depth 6-0

62'-6"

64'-0"

Future Rm
11-0x14-8

open to below

Dn

Br 3
11-6x12-0

Br 4
11-6x12-0

Second Floor
538 sq. ft.

SPECIAL FEATURES

4,120 total square feet of living area

Spacious rooms on both floors include two bedroom suites

Elaborate master bedroom with a fireplace, double walk-in closets, deluxe tub and two private entrances

Family room and kitchen form a large living area that includes a fireplace, corner window and vaulted ceiling

Bonus room above the garage is included in the square footage

4 bedrooms, 3 full baths, 2 half baths, 2-car side entry garage

Partial basement/crawl space foundation

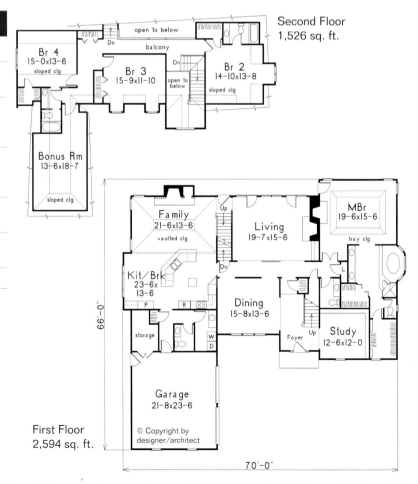

Second Floor
1,526 sq. ft.

Br 4
15-0x13-6
sloped clg

open to below

balcony

Br 3
15-9x11-10

open to below

Br 2
14-10x13-8
sloped clg

Bonus Rm
13-6x18-7

sloped clg

Family
21-6x13-6
vaulted clg

Living
19-7x15-6

MBr
19-6x15-6
tray clg

Kit/Brk
23-6x 13-6

Dining
15-8x13-6

Study
12-6x12-0

storage

Foyer

Garage
21-8x23-6

© Copyright by designer/architect

66'-0"

70'-0"

First Floor
2,594 sq. ft.

SPECIAL FEATURES

2,636 total square feet of living area

Energy efficient home with
2" x 6" exterior walls

A see-through fireplace warms the private
study and the great room equally

The large bayed dinette extends
off the kitchen and has a large wall
of windows for added sunlight

All the bedrooms are conveniently
located on the second floor for privacy

3 bedrooms, 2 1/2 baths, 3-car garage

Walk-out basement foundation

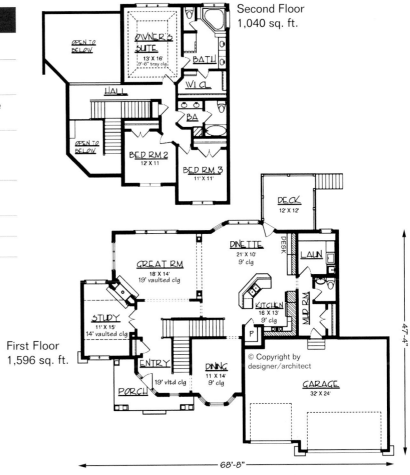

Second Floor
1,040 sq. ft.

OPEN TO BELOW

OWNER'S SUITE
13' X 16'
9'-6" tray clg

BATH

W.I.C.

HALL

BA

OPEN TO BELOW

BED RM 2
12' X 11'

BED RM 3
11' X 11'

DECK
12' X 12'

DINETTE
21' X 10'
9' clg

LAUN

DESK

GREAT RM
18' X 14'
19' vaulted clg

KITCHEN
16' X 13'
9' clg

MUD RM

STUDY
11' X 15'
14' vaulted clg

P

First Floor
1,596 sq. ft.

ENTRY

DINING
11' X 14'
9' clg

© Copyright by
designer/architect

19' vltd clg

PORCH

GARAGE
32' X 24'

47'-4"

68'-8"

SPECIAL FEATURES

2,597 total square feet of living area

Large U-shaped kitchen features an island cooktop and breakfast bar

The entry and great room are enhanced by a sweeping balcony

Bedrooms #2 and #3 share a bath, while bedroom #4 has a private bath

Vaulted great room includes transomed arch windows

2" x 6" exterior walls available, please order plan #536-007E-0001

4 bedrooms, 3 1/2 baths, 2-car side entry garage

Walk-out basement foundation, drawings also include crawl space and slab foundations

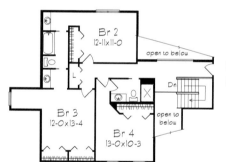

Second Floor
855 sq. ft.

Br 2
12-11x11-0

open to below

Br 3
12-0x13-4

Br 4
13-0x10-3

open to below

Dn

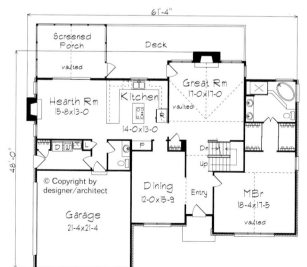

First Floor
1,742 sq. ft.

61'-4"

48'-0"

Screened Porch
vaulted

Deck

Hearth Rm
15-8x13-0

Kitchen
14-0x13-0

Great Rm
17-0x17-0
vaulted

© Copyright by designer/architect

Garage
21-4x21-4

Dining
12-0x15-9

Entry

MBr
18-4x17-5
vaulted

Dn

Up

SPECIAL FEATURES

- 3,196 total square feet of living area
- Energy efficient home with 2" x 6" exterior walls
- The cozy great room has a center fireplace flanked by bookshelves
- Double doors off the entry lead to a secluded study perfect for a home office
- The first floor owner's suite has a luxury bath and walk-in closet
- 4 bedrooms, 2 1/2 baths, 3-car garage
- Walk-out basement foundation

68'-0"

51'-4"

PORCH
13' X 10'
9' clg

DINING
15' X 11'
9' clg

GREAT RM
16' X 14'
9' clg

OWNER'S SUITE
16' X 13'
9' clg

media

LAUN

KITCHEN
14' X 14'
9' clg

W D

lockers

P

STUDY
11' X 13'
9' clg

ENTRY

BATH

GARAGE
32' X 24'

PORCH

W CL

© Copyright by designer/architect

First Floor
1,786 sq. ft.

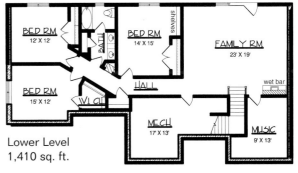

BED RM
12' X 12'

BATH

BED RM
14' X 15'

shelves

FAMILY RM
23' X 19'

BED RM
15' X 12'

W CL

HALL

wet bar

MECH
17' X 13'

MUSIC
9' X 13'

Lower Level
1,410 sq. ft.

LEGACY
SERIES

SPECIAL FEATURES

2,397 total square feet of living area

Covered entrance with fountain leads
to the double-door entry and foyer

Kitchen features two pantries and opens
into the breakfast and family rooms

Master bath features a huge
walk-in closet, electric clothes carousel,
double-bowl vanity and corner tub

3 bedrooms, 2 1/2 baths, 2-car garage

Slab foundation

Interior View - Kitchen

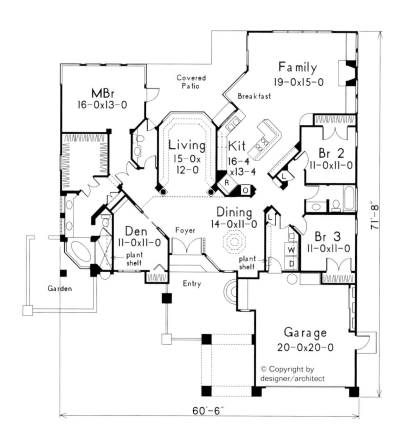

Family
19-0x15-0

Covered
Patio

Breakfast

MBr
16-0x13-0

Living
15-0x
12-0

Kit
16-4
x13-4

Br 2
11-0x11-0

Dining
14-0x11-0

Den
11-0x11-0

Foyer

Br 3
11-0x11-0

plant
shelf

plant
shelf

W
D

Garden

Entry

Garage
20-0x20-0

71'-8"

60'-6"

© Copyright by
designer/architect

SPECIAL FEATURES

2,356 total square feet of living area

A stunning bay window adds curb appeal and offers a cheerful atmosphere in the formal living room

The family room, sun room and dinette flow together with the kitchen for easy family living

Convenience is created with the garage entrance having direct access to a half bath and mud room to contain any messes

4 bedrooms, 2 1/2 baths, 2-car garage

Walk-out basement foundation

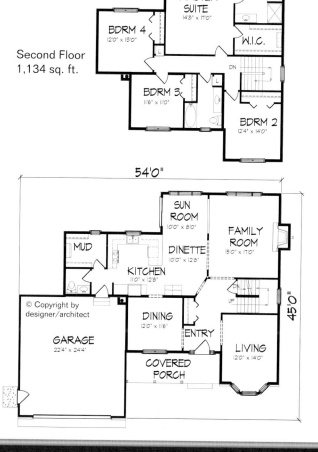

Second Floor
1,134 sq. ft.

MASTER SUITE
14'8" x 17'0"

BDRM 4
12'0" x 13'0"

W.I.C.

DN

BDRM 3
11'6" x 11'0"

BDRM 2
12'4" x 14'0"

54'0"

45'0"

SUN ROOM
10'0" x 8'0"

FAMILY ROOM
15'0" x 17'0"

MUD

DINETTE
10'0" x 12'8"

KITCHEN
11'0" x 12'8"

© Copyright by designer/architect

DINING
12'0" x 11'6"

ENTRY

DN

UP

GARAGE
22'4" x 24'4"

LIVING
12'0" x 14'0"

COVERED PORCH

First Floor
1,222 sq. ft.

LEGACY SERIES

Second Floor
1,952 sq. ft.

MASTER BEDRM.
17'-4" x 16'-4"

MSTR. BATH
16'-6" x 15'-4"

GUEST BEDRM.
10'-4" x 15'-4"

TRAY VAULT

W.I. SHWR.

W.I. CLO.
15'-0" x 8'-2"

BATH

LAUNDRY
7'-2" x 13'-10"

LIN

ARCH SOFFIT

RECESSED PICTURE NICHES

LIN

W.I. CLO.

LIN

BEDRM. 3
12'-2" x 12'-0"

W.I. CLO

BATH

BEDRM. 2
12'-2" x 12'-10"

SLOPE

SLOPE

BONUS ROOM
12'-0" x 19'-2"

KNEE WALL

KNEE WALL

BENCH SEAT

WASH AREA

BENCH SEAT

SPECIAL FEATURES

3,770 total square feet of living area

Energy efficient home with
2" x 6" exterior walls

Spacious kitchen includes a center
island with double sink and snack
bar, as well as a walk-in pantry

The sitting room near the kitchen features
a corner fireplace and has access to the
rear deck and lovely vaulted screen porch

The luxurious, second floor master suite has
abundant storage space and a plush bath

The bonus room above the garage has an
additional 256 square feet of living space

4 bedrooms, 3 1/2 baths, 3-car garage

Basement foundation

Interior View - Screen Porch

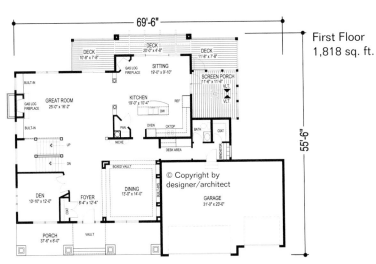

First Floor
1,818 sq. ft.

69'-6"

55'-6"

DECK
10'-8" x 7'-8"

DECK
20'-0" x 4'-8"

DECK
11'-8" x 7'-8"

GAS LOG
FIREPLACE

SITTING
19'-0" x 9'-10"

SCREEN PORCH
11'-6" x 11'-6"

VLT.

VLT.

BUILT-IN

GAS LOG
FIREPLACE

GREAT ROOM
25'-0" x 16'-2"

KITCHEN
19'-0" x 10'-4"

REF

BUILT-IN

DW

PAN

OVEN

CKTOP

BATH

COAT

NICHE

DESK AREA

BENCH/STO

UP

DN

BOXED VAULT

DEN
10'-10" x 12'-0"

FOYER
8'-4" x 12'-4"

DINING
13'-0" x 14'-0"

© Copyright by
designer/architect

BUILT-INS

GARAGE
31'-0" x 23'-0"

COAT

PORCH
37'-6" x 8'-0"

VAULT

LOWE'S **LEGACY** SERIES

SPECIAL FEATURES

2,912 total square feet of living area

Connected living and dining rooms each have full bay windows

Elegant master bedroom boasts a sitting alcove, private deck and expansive coffered ceiling

Impressive entrance and double-bay windows

Bonus room, which is included in the square footage, can become a suite with its own private bath

3 bedrooms, 3 1/2 baths, 2-car garage

Basement foundation

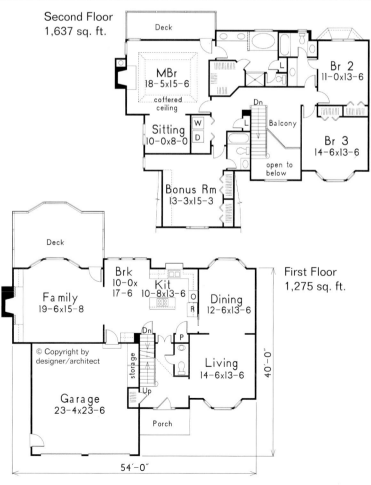

Second Floor 1,637 sq. ft.

Deck

MBr 18-5x15-6
coffered ceiling

Sitting 10-0x8-0

W D

Dn

Balcony

Br 2 11-0x13-6

L

Br 3 14-6x13-6

open to below

Bonus Rm 13-3x15-3

Deck

Brk 10-0x 17-6

Kit 10-8x13-6

Family 19-6x15-8

Dining 12-6x13-6

First Floor 1,275 sq. ft.

© Copyright by designer/architect

Dn

P

storage

Living 14-6x13-6

40'-0"

Up

Garage 23-4x23-6

Porch

54'-0"

SPECIAL FEATURES

2,738 total square feet of living area

An open entrance offers a spectacular view of the windowed rear wall and fireplace in the great room

The kitchen, breakfast and hearth rooms combine to offer an open and comfortable gathering place

The master bedroom is topped with an 11' ceiling and features a sitting alcove and deluxe bath

4 bedrooms, 3 1/2 baths, 2-car side entry garage

Basement foundation

Second Floor
823 sq. ft.

Great Room Below

Balcony

Bedroom
17' x 12'6"

Bedroom
10' x 13'10"

Bath

Bedroom
12' x 10'6"

slope ceiling   slope ceiling

First Floor
1,915 sq. ft.

Dressing

walk-in closet

Great Room
16' x 19'6"

Breakfast
14' x 11'2"

Hearth Room
17' x 14'10"

Kitchen

Laun.

Foyer

Master Bedroom
14' x 14'1"

Porch

Dining Room
12' x 13'10"

Two-car Garage
21' x 20'4"

Sitting Area
11'2" x 9'4"

© Copyright by designer/architect

48'

63'4"

SPECIAL FEATURES

3,000 total square feet of living area

Energy efficient home with
2" x 6" exterior walls

A porch with sun room style extends off
the spacious kitchen and dining area

The lower level consists of a casual family
room, a wet bar with surrounding game
area and even a place for billiards

The owner's suite is filled with extra
amenities including a private pampering
bath and a massive walk-in closet

3 bedrooms, 2 1/2 baths, 2-car
garage, 1-car side entry garage

Walk-out basement foundation

80'-0"

47'-10"

© Copyright by
designer/architect

First Floor
1,684 sq. ft.

Lower Level
1,316 sq. ft.

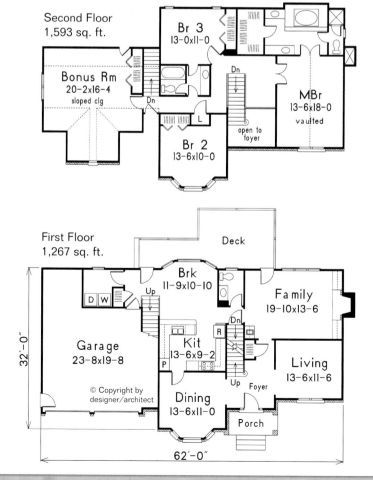

SPECIAL FEATURES

2,860 total square feet of living area

Open two-story foyer

Master bedroom suite, well isolated, includes an impressive double-door entrance

Convenient rear stairway

Private access to hall bath from bedroom #3

Bonus room above the garage is included in the square footage

3 bedrooms, 2 1/2 baths, 2-car garage

Basement foundation

Second Floor
1,593 sq. ft.

Br 3
13-0x11-0

Bonus Rm
20-2x16-4
sloped clg

MBr
13-6x18-0
vaulted

Br 2
13-6x10-0

Dn

L

Dn

open to foyer

First Floor
1,267 sq. ft.

Deck

Brk
11-9x10-10

Family
19-10x13-6

D W

Up

Garage
23-8x19-8

Kit
13-6x9-2

R

Dn

Living
13-6x11-6

P

Up

Foyer

© Copyright by designer/architect

Dining
13-6x11-0

Porch

32'-0"

62'-0"

SPECIAL FEATURES

2,887 total square feet of living area

Energy efficient home with
2" x 6" exterior walls

A cozy hearth room shares a
prominent see-through fireplace
with the great room offering the
perfect spot for casual relaxation

Double doors off the entry hall lead
into a secluded and handsome study
with a built-in desk and bookshelves

The relaxing owner's suite offers a
generous walk-in closet, double-bowl
vanity, amazing walk-in shower and a
spa-like tub to soak your cares away

4 bedrooms, 2 1/2 baths, 4-car garage

Walk-out basement foundation

Second Floor
1,437 sq. ft.

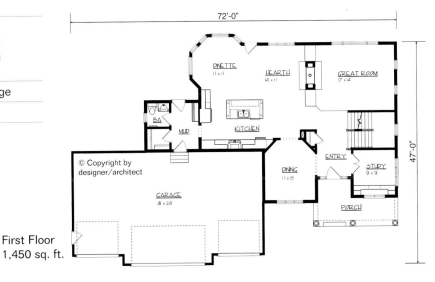

© Copyright by
designer/architect

First Floor
1,450 sq. ft.

SPECIAL FEATURES

3,109 total square feet of living area

Energy efficient home with
2" x 6" exterior walls

A double-door entry elegantly leads into this
home and back into the stunning great room

Homeowners will enjoy the openness of the
combined kitchen, nook and great room

Relax in the master bedroom suite equipped
with a pampering bath and walk-in closet

4 bedrooms, 2 1/2 baths,
3 1/2-car side entry garage

Basement foundation

Second Floor
885 sq. ft.

OPEN TO
GRT. RM.

BR #2
11'4" X 16'4"

BR #3
11'0" X 16'6"

OPEN TO
E.

BR #4
12'6" X 14'4"

First Floor
2,224 sq. ft.

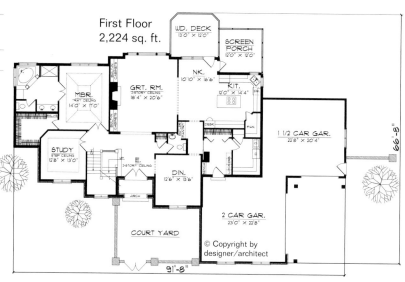

W.D. DECK
13'0" X 12'0"

SCREEN
PORCH
12'0" X 12'0"

MBR.
14'0" X 17'0"

GRT. RM.
2-STORY CEILING
18'4" X 20'6"

NK.
10'10" X 16'6"

KIT.
12'0" X 14'4"

STUDY
STEP CEILING
12'8" X 13'0"

E.
2-STORY CEILING

DIN.
12'6" X 13'6"

1 1/2 CAR GAR.
22'8" X 20'4"

2 CAR GAR.
23'0" X 22'8"

COURT YARD

© Copyright by
designer/architect

66'-8"

91'-8"

Rear View

SPECIAL FEATURES

3,144 total square feet of living area

9' ceilings on the first floor

Kitchen offers a large pantry, island cooktop and close proximity to the laundry and dining rooms

Expansive family room includes a wet bar, fireplace and an attractive bay window

4 bedrooms, 3 1/2 baths, 3-car side entry garage

Basement foundation

Second Floor
1,420 sq. ft.

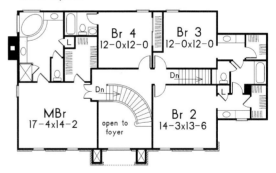

Br 4
12-0x12-0

Br 3
12-0x12-0

MBr
17-4x14-2

open to foyer

Br 2
14-3x13-6

Dn

Dn

First Floor
1,724 sq. ft.

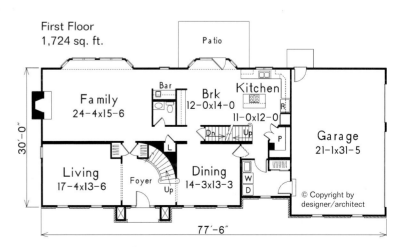

Patio

Family
24-4x15-6

Bar

Brk
12-0x14-0

Kitchen

11-0x12-0

Garage
21-1x31-5

Living
17-4x13-6

Foyer

Up

Dn

Up

Dining
14-3x13-3

W
D

P

30'-0"

77'-6"

© Copyright by designer/architect

0

LEGACY
SERIES

SPECIAL FEATURES

2,697 total square feet of living area

Energy efficient home with
2" x 6" exterior walls

A popular porch space shares a see-through
fireplace with the great room offering
the perfect spot for casual relaxation

Double doors off the entry hall lead into a
secluded and handsome study with plenty
of privacy when working from home

All the bedrooms are located on the
second floor for convenient family living

4 bedrooms, 2 1/2 baths, 3-car garage

Walk-out basement foundation

Second Floor
1,314 sq. ft.

BED RM 2
13 x 10

OWNERS SUITE
15 x 15

BATH

W.I.C.

BED RM 4
12 x 10

LAUN

BATH

BED RM 3
12 x 10

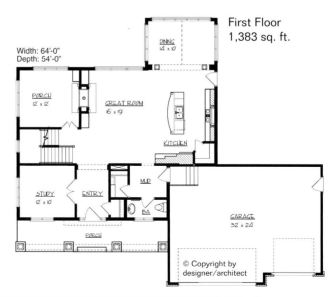

First Floor
1,383 sq. ft.

Width: 64'-0"
Depth: 54'-0"

DINING
14 x 10

PORCH
12 x 12

GREAT ROOM
16 x 19

KITCHEN

STUDY
12 x 10

ENTRY

MUD

BA

GARAGE
32 x 24

PORCH

SPECIAL FEATURES

2,846 total square feet of living area

9' ceilings on the first floor
and 8' ceilings on the second floor

Prominent double-bay windows
and two-story foyer add brightness
and space to both floors

Master bedroom with double-door
entry and coffered ceiling includes an
elaborate bath with large tub, separate
shower and individual walk-in closets

Bonus room over the garage is
included in the square footage

4 bedrooms, 2 1/2 baths,
2-car side entry garage

Basement foundation, drawings also
include slab and crawl space foundations

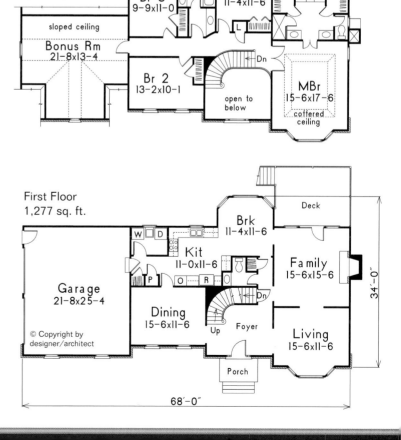

Second Floor
1,569 sq. ft.

Br 3
9-9x11-0

Br 4
11-4x11-6

sloped ceiling

Bonus Rm
21-8x13-4

Br 2
13-2x10-1

Dn

open to
below

MBr
15-6x17-6
coffered
ceiling

First Floor
1,277 sq. ft.

Deck

Brk
11-4x11-6

Kit
11-0x11-6

Family
15-6x15-6

Garage
21-8x25-4

© Copyright by
designer/architect

P

O   R

Dn

34'-0"

Dining
15-6x11-6

Up   Foyer

Living
15-6x11-6

Porch

68'-0"

89

SPECIAL FEATURES

3,117 total square feet of living area

Energy efficient home with
2" x 6" exterior walls

The cheerful kitchen has a double-bowl
sink in the island, a large pantry and
opens up nicely to the dinette area

The centralized fireplace is flanked
by bookshelves in the great room

The relaxing owner's bedroom offers a
bath with a generous closet, double-bowl
vanity, amazing walk-in shower and a
spa-style tub to soak your cares away

3 bedrooms, 2 1/2 baths, 2-car garage

Slab foundation

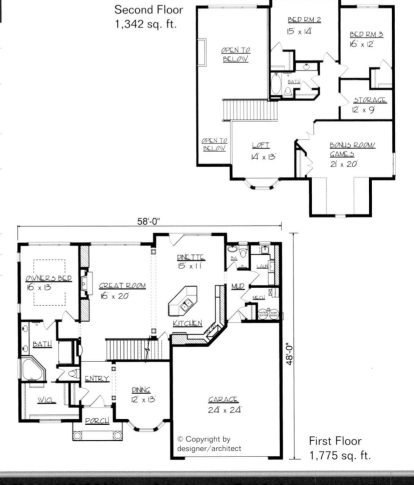

Second Floor
1,342 sq. ft.

First Floor
1,775 sq. ft.

© Copyright by
designer/architect

SPECIAL FEATURES

2,696 total square feet of living area

Magnificent master bedroom features a private covered porch and luxurious bath

Second floor game room includes balcony access and an adjacent loft

Well-planned kitchen includes a walk-in pantry, island cooktop and nearby spacious breakfast room

4 bedrooms, 3 baths, 2-car side entry garage

Slab foundation, drawings also include crawl space foundation

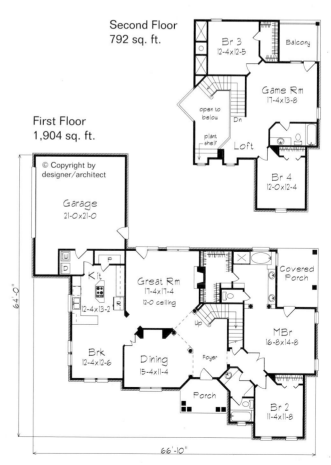

Second Floor
792 sq. ft.

Br 3
12-4x12-5

Balcony

Game Rm
17-4x13-8

open to below

Dn

plant shelf

Loft

Br 4
12-0x12-4

First Floor
1,904 sq. ft.

© Copyright by designer/architect

Garage
21-0x21-0

64'-0"

Kit
12-4x13-2

Great Rm
17-4x17-4
12-0 ceiling

Covered Porch

MBr
16-8x14-8

Brk
12-4x12-6

Dining
15-4x11-4

Foyer

up

Porch

Br 2
11-4x11-8

66'-10"

SPECIAL FEATURES

4,160 total square feet of living area

The cozy sitting area off the breakfast room offers a comfortable space for relaxation

The master bedroom pleases with its private sitting alcove, entry to the rear deck and elegant dressing area

The lower level is an inviting space to spend fun times with an exercise room, two additional bedrooms, a wet bar and space for a game table and media area

3 bedrooms, 2 1/2 baths, 2-car side entry garage

Walk-out basement foundation

Rear View

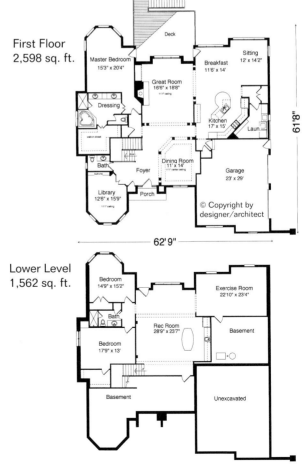

First Floor
2,598 sq. ft.

Deck

Master Bedroom
15'3" x 20'4"

Sitting
12' x 14'2"

Breakfast
11'6" x 14'

Great Room
16'6" x 18'8"
11'1" center ceiling

Dressing

Kitchen
17' x 15'

Laun.

walk-in closet

Bath

Foyer

Dining Room
11' x 14'
11'1" center ceiling

Garage
23' x 29'

Library
12'6" x 15'9"
11'1" ceiling

Porch

© Copyright by
designer/architect

61'8"

62' 9"

Lower Level
1,562 sq. ft.

Bedroom
14'9" x 15'2"

Exercise Room
22'10" x 23'4"

Bath

Rec Room
28'9" x 23'7"

Basement

Bedroom
17'9" x 13'

Basement

Unexcavated

SPECIAL FEATURES

2,908 total square feet of living area

Energy efficient home with
2" x 6" exterior walls

The open kitchen enjoys an angled center
island with a double sink that overlooks
the cheerful dining and sitting rooms

Built-ins surround the fireplace
in the cozy great room

The owner's bedroom includes a
sun-filled private sitting area and its own
bath with a double-bowl vanity, amazing
walk-in shower and a whirlpool tub

4 bedrooms, 2 1/2 baths, 3-car garage

Walk-out basement foundation

Second Floor
1,533 sq. ft.

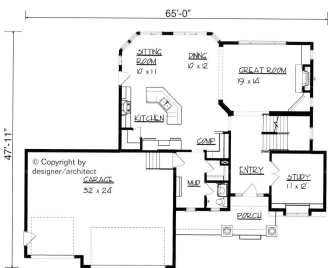

First Floor
1,375 sq. ft.

© Copyright by
designer/architect

LEGACY
SERIES

Second Floor
855 sq. ft.

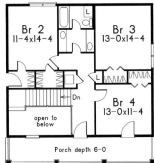

Br 2
11-4x14-4

Br 3
13-0x14-4

Br 4
13-0x11-4

Dn

open to below

Porch depth 6-0

SPECIAL FEATURES

2,605 total square feet of living area

Energy efficient home
with 2" x 6" exterior walls

Master bedroom boasts a vaulted
ceiling and transom picture window
that brightens the sitting area

Country kitchen features appliances set in
between brick dividers and a beamed ceiling

Living room features built-in bookcases,
fireplace and a raised tray ceiling

4 bedrooms, 2 1/2 baths,
2-car side entry garage

Slab foundation, drawings also include
crawl space and basement foundations

Exterior View - Front Entry

First Floor
1,750 sq. ft.

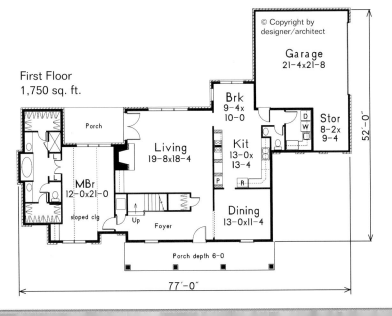

© Copyright by
designer/architect

Garage
21-4x21-8

Brk
9-4x
10-0

Stor
8-2x
9-4

Porch

Living
19-8x18-4

Kit
13-0x
13-4

MBr
12-0x21-0

sloped clg

Up

Foyer

Dining
13-0x11-4

Porch depth 6-0

52'-0"

77'-0"

LEGACY
SERIES

SPECIAL FEATURES

2,403 total square feet of living area

The master bedroom has a
9' ceiling that raises to 11' in
the octagon-shaped sitting area

Kitchen is enhanced by a breakfast bar
area, center island and extra-large pantry

Multiple windows in the breakfast
area create a cheerful environment

4 bedrooms, 3 1/2 baths,
2-car side entry garage

Basement foundation, drawings
also include slab foundation

Second Floor
693 sq. ft.

high glass

Bedroom
11'4" x 12'6"

Bath

Great Room
Below

Hall

high ceiling

linen

Bedroom
10' x 13'10"

Bath

plant shelf

walk-in
closet

Bedroom
12' x 10'6"

slope
ceiling

slope
ceiling

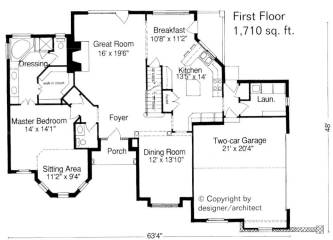

First Floor
1,710 sq. ft.

Breakfast
10'8" x 11'2"

Great Room
16' x 19'6"

Kitchen
13'5" x 14'

Dressing

walk-in closet

pantry

Laun.

Master Bedroom
14' x 14'1"

Foyer

Two-car Garage
21' x 20'4"

48'

Porch

Dining Room
12' x 13'10"

Sitting Area
11'2" x 9'4"

© Copyright by
designer/architect

63'4"

LEGACY
SERIES

SPECIAL FEATURES

2,816 total square feet of living area

Enormous master bath has a beautiful corner whirlpool tub and an oversized walk-in closet

Large center island in the kitchen is angled for interest and helps combine the space with the breakfast room

Lots of windows brighten the great room

Bonus room on the second floor has an additional 325 square feet of living area

3 bedrooms, 2 full baths, 2 half baths, 3-car side entry garage

Walk-out basement foundation

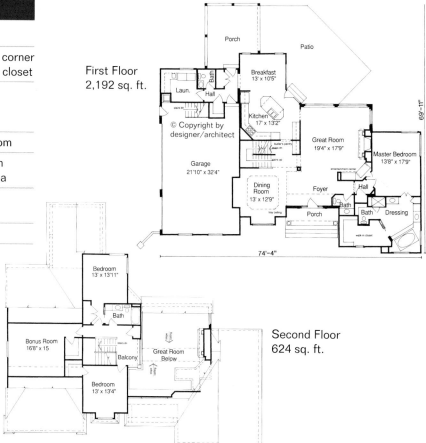

First Floor
2,192 sq. ft.

Second Floor
624 sq. ft.

SPECIAL FEATURES

3,242 total square feet of living area

Energy efficient home
with 2" x 6" exterior walls

An enormous bayed dining room has
an entire wall of built-ins perfect
for storage and cookbooks

Double doors off the entry lead to a
secluded study perfect for a home office

A large angled counter in the kitchen
overlooks the bayed dining area
and beyond to the great room

5 bedrooms, 2 1/2 baths, 3-car garage

Basement foundation

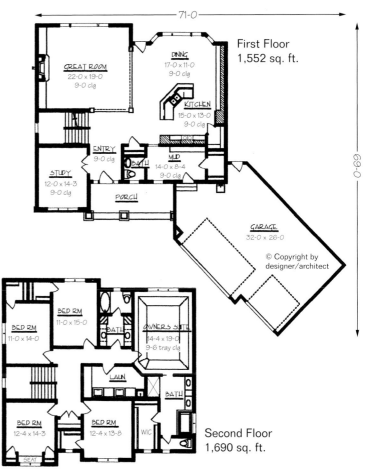

First Floor
1,552 sq. ft.

GREAT ROOM
22-0 x 19-0
9-0 clg

DINNG
17-0 x 11-0
9-0 clg

KITCHEN
15-0 x 13-0
9-0 clg

ENTRY
9-0 clg

STUDY
12-0 x 14-3
9-0 clg

BATH

MUD
14-0 x 8-4
9-0 clg

PORCH

GARAGE
32-0 x 26-0

© Copyright by
designer/architect

Second Floor
1,690 sq. ft.

BED RM
11-0 x 14-0

BED RM
11-0 x 15-0

BATH

OWNER'S SUITE
14-4 x 19-0
9-6 tray clg

LAUN

BATH

BED RM
12-4 x 14-3

BED RM
12-4 x 13-8

WIC

SEAT

71-0

69-0

LOWE'S **LEGACY** SERIES

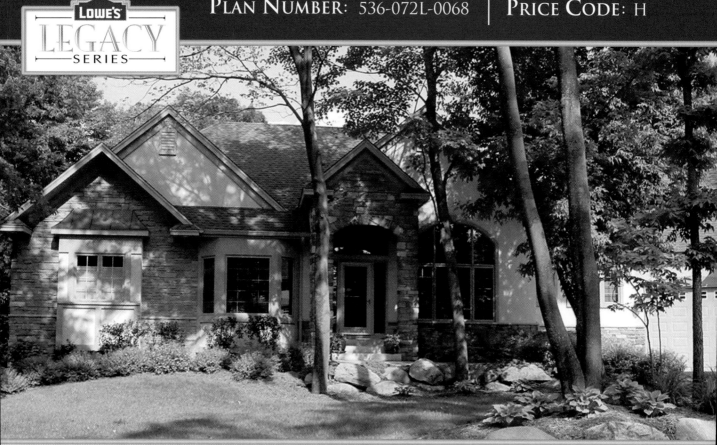

SPECIAL FEATURES

3,918 total square feet of living area

Energy efficient home with
2" x 6" exterior walls

Stone decorates the facade of
this elegant ranch home

A bay window accents the quiet study,
deluxe owner's suite and charming dinette

An open family room connects to the
billiards area complete with a bar, making
a lower level perfect for entertaining

3 bedrooms, 2 1/2 baths, 3-car garage

Walk-out basement foundation

First Floor
2,228 sq. ft.

Lower Level
1,690 sq. ft.

© Copyright by
designer/architect

SPECIAL FEATURES

2,416 total square feet of living area

The large grand entry invites guests in and steps lead to the grand family room

Tray ceilings adorn both the master suite and luxurious bath creating a feeling of elegance

A built-in TV cabinet is located next to the cozy fireplace in the family room

Bonus room on the second floor has an additional 243 square feet of living area

3 bedrooms, 2 1/2 baths, 3-car garage

Basement foundation

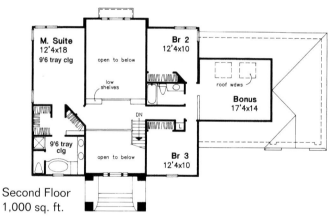

M. Suite
12'4x18
9'6 tray clg

open to below

low shelves

Br 2
12'4x10

roof wdws

Bonus
17'4x14

9'6 tray clg

open to below

DN

Br 3
12'4x10

Second Floor
1,000 sq. ft.

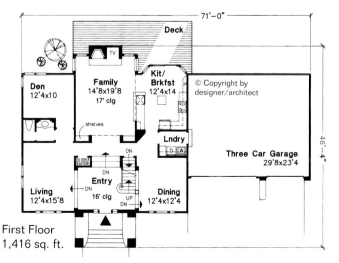

71'-0"

Deck

TV

Den
12'4x10

Family
14'8x19'8
17' clg

Kit/
Brkfst
12'4x14

© Copyright by
designer/architect

shelves

Lndry

46'-4"

Three Car Garage
29'8x23'4

Living
12'4x15'8

DN
DN
DN
Entry
16' clg
UP
DN

Dining
12'4x12'4

First Floor
1,416 sq. ft.

SPECIAL FEATURES

2,400 total square feet of living area

Airy, spacious, highly-functional design for carefree living

Master bedroom suite is located on the first floor for added privacy

Extensive porch and deck combination for outdoor entertaining

3 bedrooms, 2 1/2 baths, 2-car garage

Crawl space foundation

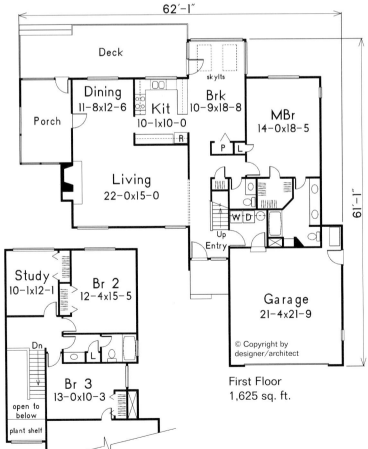

62'-1"

Deck

Dining
11-8x12-6

Kit
10-1x10-0

Brk
10-9x18-8

MBr
14-0x18-5

Porch

sk ylts

R

P L

Living
22-0x15-0

W D

Up
Entry

61'-1"

Garage
21-4x21-9

© Copyright by
designer/architect

First Floor
1,625 sq. ft.

Study
10-1x12-1

Br 2
12-4x15-5

Dn

L

Br 3
13-0x10-3

open to
below

plant shelf

Second Floor
775 sq. ft.

SPECIAL FEATURES

3,034 total square feet of living area

Step-down into a huge family room with fireplace, built-in shelves, cabinets and deck access

Functional U-shaped kitchen, dining and breakfast rooms with adjoining screened porch are all cleverly built into bay windows

The second floor has a vaulted master bedroom with luxury bath and double walk-in closets, balcony view of staircase bay and an additional three bedrooms with bath

4 bedrooms, 2 1/2 baths, 2-car side entry garage

Walk-out basement foundation

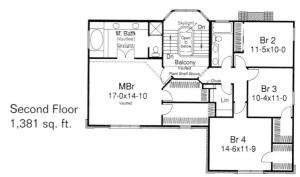

Second Floor
1,381 sq. ft.

First Floor
1,653 sq. ft.

SPECIAL FEATURES

2,614 total square feet of living area

A large front entry leads to a vaulted great room featuring an atrium, fireplace and a massive two-story window wall

The kitchen offers a snack bar peninsula, island counter and walk-in pantry

Both a covered and uncovered deck plus a sunroom are restful areas one may enjoy adjacent to the bayed breakfast room

The master bedroom enjoys a coffered ceiling, bay window, plush bath and huge walk-in closet

3 bedrooms, 2 1/2 baths, 3-car side entry garage

Walk-out basement foundation

Rear View

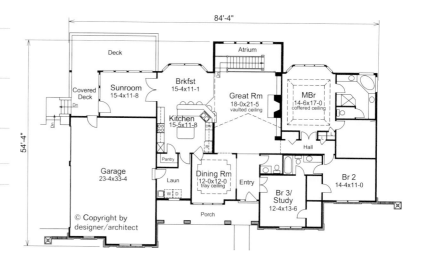

84'-4"

54'-4"

Deck

Covered Deck

Sunroom
15-4x11-8

Brkfst
15-4x11-1

Atrium

Great Rm
18-0x21-5
vaulted ceiling

MBr
14-6x17-0
coffered ceiling

Kitchen
15-5x11-8

Pantry

Garage
23-4x33-4

Laun

W D

Dining Rm
12-0x12-0
tray ceiling

Entry

Hall

Br 2
14-4x11-0

Br 3/
Study
12-4x13-6

Porch

© Copyright by
designer/architect

SPECIAL FEATURES

2,610 total square feet of living space

A 10' cabinet peninsula divides the large dining area from a functional kitchen featuring an abundance of storage and counterspace

Bookshelves flanking a masonry fireplace adorn the end of a spacious family room

All second floor bedrooms have ample storage

Optional studio above the garage has an additional 254 square feet of living area

Master bedroom includes two closets and a full bath

4 bedrooms, 2 1/2 baths, 2-car side entry garage

Basement foundation

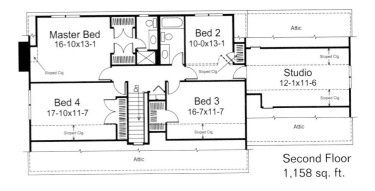

Master Bed
16-10x13-1

Bed 2
10-0x13-1

Attic

Sloped Clg.

Studio
12-1x11-6

Sloped Clg.

Bed 4
17-10x11-7

Bed 3
16-7x11-7

Sloped Clg.

Sloped Clg.

Attic

Attic

Second Floor
1,158 sq. ft.

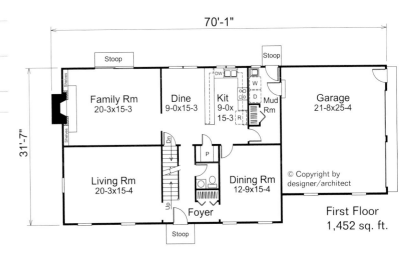

70'-1"

31'-7"

Stoop

Stoop

Family Rm
20-3x15-3

Dine
9-0x15-3

Kit
9-0x
15-3

Mud
Rm

Garage
21-8x25-4

Living Rm
20-3x15-4

P

Dining Rm
12-9x15-4

© Copyright by
designer/architect

Foyer

Stoop

First Floor
1,452 sq. ft.

SPECIAL FEATURES

3,670 total square feet of living area

Multiple gables, detailed brickwork and front patio establish an impressive facade

Two-story entry has a handcrafted staircase and leads to a fabulous great room with fireplace flanked by shelving

The kitchen features a snack bar island, computer desk, breakfast room with bay window and a walk-in pantry

An awesome bath with two huge walk-in closets accompanies the master bedroom suite

The second floor is comprised of three bedrooms, each with their own bath and walk-in closets as well as an open playroom with balcony overlook

4 bedrooms, 4 1/2 baths, 3-car side entry garage

Basement foundation

Second Floor
1,347 sq. ft.

First Floor
2,323 sq. ft.

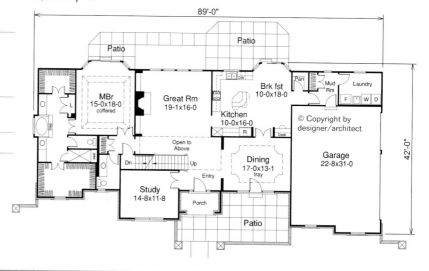

© Copyright by designer/architect

SPECIAL FEATURES

2,284 total square feet of living area

This design appears to have only a 3-car garage, but stores and displays up to 12 mid-size autos plus one small RV in the lower and upper garages

The upper garage has a workshop with toilet while the lower garage is open for car maneuvering and placement with light from three 9' glass sliding doors, ideal as a showroom

The lower garage is also great for small business storage with an enclosed ramp making loading/unloading a breeze

3 bedrooms, 2 1/2 baths, 12-car garage, 1-RV garage

Walk-out basement foundation

Interior View - Lower Garage

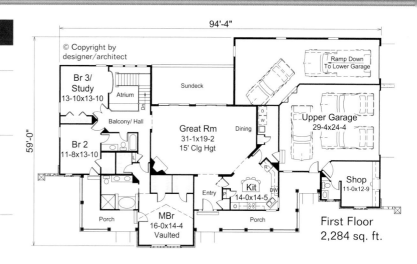

94'-4"

© Copyright by designer/architect

Ramp Down To Lower Garage

Br 3/ Study 13-10x13-10

Atrium

Sundeck

Upper Garage 29-4x24-4

59'-0"

Balcony/ Hall

Great Rm 31-1x19-2 15' Clg Hgt

Dining

Br 2 11-8x13-10

Shop 11-0x12-9

Entry

Kit 14-0x14-5

Porch

MBr 16-0x14-4 Vaulted

Porch

First Floor 2,284 sq. ft.

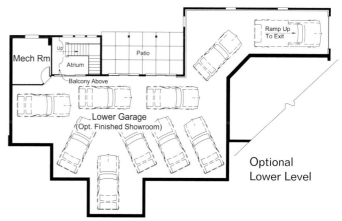

Ramp Up To Exit

Mech Rm

Atrium

Patio

Balcony Above

Lower Garage (Opt. Finished Showroom)

Optional Lower Level

SPECIAL FEATURES

3,420 total square feet of living area

Hip roofs, elliptical windows and brick facade with quoins emphasize stylish sophisticated living

Grand foyer has flared staircase in addition to secondary stair from the kitchen

Enormous kitchen features a cooktop island, walk-in pantry, angled breakfast bar and computer desk

Splendid gallery connects family room and wet bar with vaulted hearth room

Master bedroom has a coffered ceiling, double walk-in closets and a lavish bath

4 bedrooms, 3 1/2 baths, 3-car rear entry garage

Walk-out basement foundation

Second Floor
1,526 sq. ft.

Br 2
14-0x12-0

Br 3
12-9x13-4

MBr
14-0x15-7

Dn

Dn

Br 4
11-8x12-0

Foyer

Porch

First Floor
1,894 sq. ft.

80'-0"

52'-0"

Deck

Hearth
14-0x17-8
vaulted

Gallery

Kit
17-5x13-8

Brk

Family
18-0x18-10

© Copyright by designer/architect

Dn

P

R

OVEN

Up

Garage
29-4x21-4

Living
14-0x12-0

Foyer

Dining
14-0x12-0

W
D

Up

Porch

SPECIAL FEATURES

2,887 total square feet of living area

Columned foyer opens into the living room which has a sunken wet bar that extends into the pool area

Stunning master bedroom accesses the patio and offers a view of the pool through a curved window wall

Dining room boasts window walls

Second floor includes two bedrooms, a bath and shared balcony deck overlooking the pool area

3 bedrooms, 3 baths, 2-car garage

Slab foundation

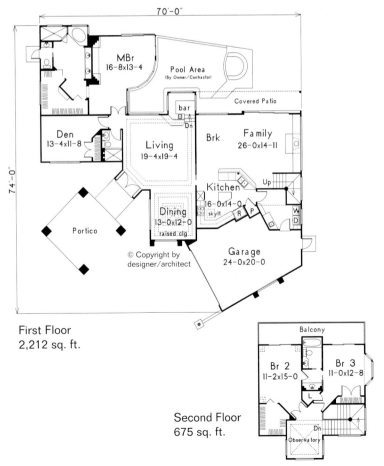

70'-0"

74'-0"

MBr
16-8x13-4

Pool Area
(By Owner/Contractor)

Covered Patio

bar
Dn

Den
13-4x11-8

Living
19-4x19-4

Brk

Family
26-0x14-11

Kitchen
16-0x14-0
skylt

Up

R P

W
D

Dining
13-0x12-0
raised clg

Portico

© Copyright by
designer/architect

Garage
24-0x20-0

First Floor
2,212 sq. ft.

Balcony

Br 2
11-2x15-0

Br 3
11-0x12-8

L

Dn

Observatory

Second Floor
675 sq. ft.

LEGACY
SERIES

SPECIAL FEATURES

3,641 total square feet of living area

Secluded family room includes a large fireplace, patio sliding doors and easy access to the kitchen and dining room

The front of the home consists of a formal living room and an adjacent library for quiet time

Focal point of the second floor is a large central sitting room that is perfect as a children's play area or an office

Covered front porch adds charm to the design

5 bedrooms, 4 baths, 3-car side entry garage

Basement foundation

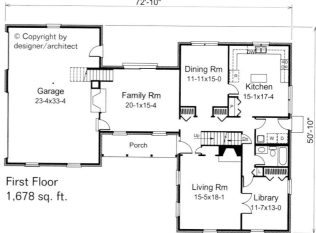

Br 4
13-5x12-2

Dn

MBr
13-5x20-3

Sitting Rm
17-11x15-4

Br 5
13-5x17-0

Second Floor
1,963 sq. ft.

Br 2
11-0x14-6

Br 3
10-1x12-1

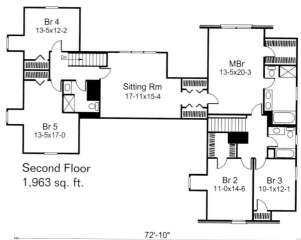

72'-10"

© Copyright by designer/architect

Garage
23-4x33-4

Family Rm
20-1x15-4

Dining Rm
11-11x15-0

Kitchen
15-1x17-4

Up

Dn

W D

Porch

50'-10"

First Floor
1,678 sq. ft.

Living Rm
15-5x18-1

Library
11-7x13-0

SPECIAL FEATURES

2,491 total square feet of living area

Energy efficient home with
2" x 6" exterior walls

Entry is flanked by formal
living and dining rooms

Hallway between dining room and
kitchen includes a butler's pantry
to ease serving a party

The kitchen, breakfast nook and family room
combine for an expansive gathering space

All bedrooms are located on the
second floor for privacy

4 bedrooms, 2 1/2 baths,
2-car side entry garage

Basement foundation

Second Floor
1,158 sq. ft.

BR.3
10'6"x11'8"

BR.2
10'4"x11'8"

MBR.
TRAY CEILING
15'x19'0"

DOWN

OPEN TO
FOYER

BR.4
CATHEDRAL CEILING
13'x13'6"

First Floor
1,333 sq. ft.

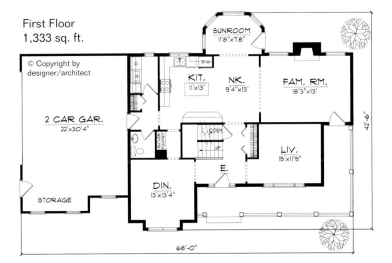

SUNROOM
11'8"x7'8"

© Copyright by
designer/architect

KIT.
11'x13'

NK.
9'4"x13'

FAM. RM.
18'3"x13'

2 CAR GAR.
22'x30'4"

BUTLER
PANTRY

DOWN

UP

LIV.
15'x11'9"

DIN.
13'x13'4"

E.

STORAGE

42'-6"

68'-0"

SPECIAL FEATURES

3,200 total square feet of living area

Two-story foyer and graceful curved stairway are flanked by separate living and dining rooms

Master bedroom suite on the second floor has a double-door entry, fireplace and a bath with a step-up tub built into the bay window

4 bedrooms, 2 1/2 baths, 2-car side entry garage

Basement foundation

MBr
15-4x17-0

Br 2
13-9x14-0

Second Floor
1,514 sq. ft.

Dn

open to
below

Br 4
13-1x12-0

Br 3
13-5x15-0

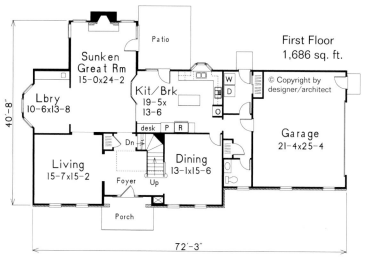

Sunken
Great Rm
15-0x24-2

Patio

First Floor
1,686 sq. ft.

Lbry
10-6x13-8

Kit/Brk
19-5x
13-6

W
D

© Copyright by
designer/architect

desk   P   R

Dn

Garage
21-4x25-4

Living
15-7x15-2

Dining
13-1x15-6

Foyer

Up

Porch

40'-8"

72'-3"

SPECIAL FEATURES

3,974 total square feet of living area

The exterior offers a look of distinction from the use of fancy brickwork to the old-world stone

A fireplace and wood beam ceiling adorn the large great room

The huge master bedroom features a vaulted ceiling, fireplace, two walk-in closets and a lavish bath

4 bedrooms, 3 1/2 baths, 3-car side entry garage

Basement foundation

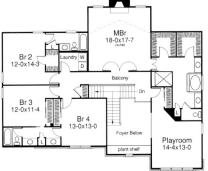

Second Floor
1,950 sq. ft.

MBr
18-0x17-7
vaulted

Br 2
12-0x14-3

Laundry W D

Balcony

Br 3
12-0x11-4

Dn

Br 4
13-0x13-0

Foyer Below

plant shelf

Playroom
14-4x13-0

First Floor
2,024 sq. ft.

65'-0"

65'-8"

Patio

Patio

Great Room
18-0x21-3

Study
14-4x14-1

Brk'ft Room
12-3x18-0

Kitchen
12-0x18-0

Up

Dn

Dining
15-1x13-0
tray clg

Up

Foyer

Living Room
14-4x17-4

Mud Rm

Porch

Porch

© Copyright by
designer/architect

Garage
21-4x29-4

SPECIAL FEATURES

2,397 total square feet of living area

Varied ceiling heights throughout home

All bedrooms boast walk-in closets

Garage includes convenient storage area

Angled kitchen counter overlooks the spacious living room with fireplace

Master bedroom has a coffered ceiling and luxurious bath

4 bedrooms, 3 baths, 2-car side entry garage

Slab foundation

Rear View

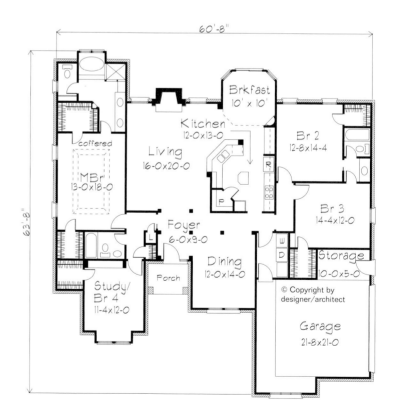

60'-8"

63'-8"

coffered

MBr
13-0x18-0

Living
16-0x20-0

Kitchen
12-0x13-0

Brkfast
10' x 10'

Br 2
12-8x14-4

Br 3
14-4x12-0

Foyer
6-0x9-0

Dining
12-0x14-0

Storage
10-0x5-0

Porch

Study/
Br 4
11-4x12-0

© Copyright by
designer/architect

Garage
21-8x21-0

SPECIAL FEATURES

3,269 total square feet of living area

Stately stonework, cedar shakes and clipped gables combine to create a captivating facade

A large country porch has access to the garage

The grand-sized family room, open to the sunny breakfast room, features a fireplace, lots of windows and a convenient adjacent powder room

A sensationally designed kitchen includes all the amenities

4 bedrooms, 3 1/2 baths, 2-car garage

Basement foundation

Second Floor
1,594 sq. ft.

First Floor
1,675 sq. ft.

© Copyright by designer/architect

SPECIAL FEATURES

2,518 total square feet of living area

Expansive kitchen is adjacent
to the breakfast room

Sophisticated master bedroom
is complemented by double
closets and a luxury bath

Family room enjoys rear views
and a stately fireplace

Secondary porch leads to the mud room
with laundry, utility sink and coat closet

4 bedrooms, 2 1/2 baths,
2-car side entry garage

Partial basement/crawl space
foundation, drawings also include
crawl space and slab foundations

Second Floor
816 sq. ft.

First Floor
1,702 sq. ft.

© Copyright by
designer/architect

SPECIAL FEATURES

2,340 total square feet of living area

Large family room has a vaulted ceiling and bookshelves that surround the brick fireplace

Highly functional kitchen is easily accessible from many parts of this home

The second floor consists of two secondary bedrooms each having direct access to the bath

The loft can serve as a recreation area or fifth bedroom

3 bedrooms, 2 1/2 baths, 2-car side entry garage

Walk-out basement foundation

Second Floor
651 sq. ft.

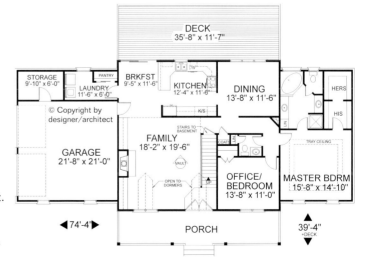

First Floor
1,689 sq. ft.

◄ 74'-4" ►

39'-4"
+DECK

© Copyright by designer/architect

SPECIAL FEATURES

2,617 total square feet of living area

Combination dining and living rooms provide a relaxing atmosphere

Kitchen/dinette area overlooks the large family room with fireplace

Sunny master bedroom is loaded with amenities such as a walk-in closet and luxurious private bath with step-up garden tub

Covered front porch is a handy feature

4 bedrooms, 2 1/2 baths, 2-car garage

Basement foundation

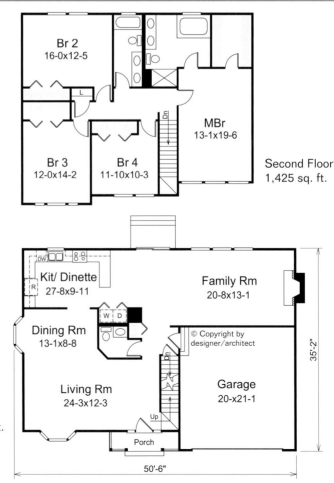

Br 2
16-0x12-5

MBr
13-1x19-6

Br 3
12-0x14-2

Br 4
11-10x10-3

Second Floor
1,425 sq. ft.

Kit/ Dinette
27-8x9-11

Family Rm
20-8x13-1

Dining Rm
13-1x8-8

© Copyright by
designer/architect

Living Rm
24-3x12-3

Garage
20-x21-1

Up

Porch

First Floor
1,192 sq. ft.

35'-2"

50'-6"

SPECIAL FEATURES

3,427 total square feet of living area

10' ceilings on the first floor

Elaborate master bedroom features a
coffered ceiling and luxurious private bath

Two-story showplace foyer is flanked
by the dining and living rooms

Bonus room above the garage is
included in the square footage

4 bedrooms, 3 1/2 baths,
2-car side entry garage

Basement foundation

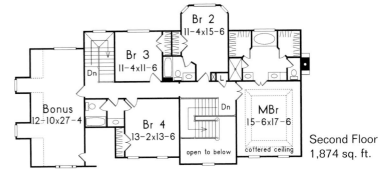

Br 2
11-4x15-6

Br 3
11-4x11-6

Dn

Bonus
12-10x27-4

Br 4
13-2x13-6

open to below

MBr
15-6x17-6

coffered ceiling

Dn

Second Floor
1,874 sq. ft.

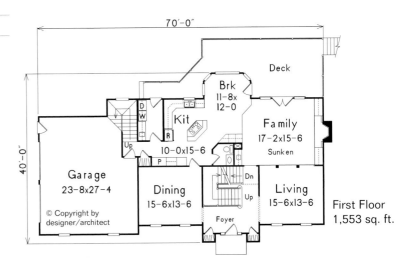

70'-0"

40'-0"

Deck

Brk
11-8x
12-0

Kit
10-0x15-6

Family
17-2x15-6
Sunken

DW

Up

R

P

Garage
23-8x27-4

© Copyright by
designer/architect

Dining
15-6x13-6

Dn

Up

Foyer

Living
15-6x13-6

First Floor
1,553 sq. ft.

SPECIAL FEATURES

2,723 total square feet of living area

A large porch invites you into an elegant foyer which accesses a vaulted study with private hall and coat closet

Great room is second to none, comprised of a fireplace, built-in shelves, vaulted ceiling and a 1 1/2 story window wall

A spectacular hearth room with vaulted ceiling and masonry fireplace opens to an elaborate kitchen featuring two snack bars, a cooking island and walk-in pantry

4 bedrooms, 2 1/2 baths, 3-car side entry garage

Basement foundation

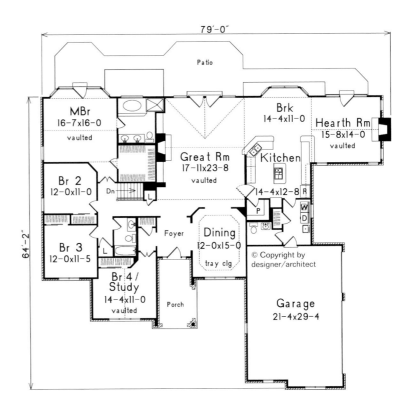

79'-0"

64'-2"

Patio

MBr
16-7x16-0
vaulted

Brk
14-4x11-0

Hearth Rm
15-8x14-0
vaulted

Great Rm
17-11x23-8
vaulted

Kitchen
14-4x12-8

Br 2
12-0x11-0

Dn

Br 3
12-0x11-5

Foyer

Dining
12-0x15-0
tray clg

© Copyright by
designer/architect

Br 4 /
Study
14-4x11-0
vaulted

Porch

Garage
21-4x29-4

SPECIAL FEATURES

2,461 total square feet of living area

Unique corner tub, double vanities and walk-in closet enhance the large master bedroom

Fireplace provides focus in the spacious family room

Centrally located half bath for guests

4 bedrooms, 2 1/2 baths, 2-car garage

Basement foundation, drawings also include slab and crawl space foundations

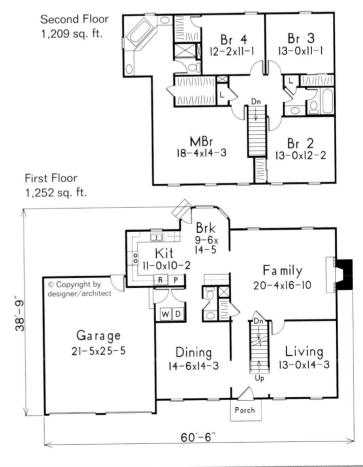

Second Floor
1,209 sq. ft.

Br 4
12-2x11-1

Br 3
13-0x11-1

L

Dn

L

MBr
18-4x14-3

Br 2
13-0x12-2

First Floor
1,252 sq. ft.

Brk
9-6x14-5

Kit
11-0x10-2

R P

Family
20-4x16-10

© Copyright by designer/architect

W D

Garage
21-5x25-5

Dn

38'-9"

Dining
14-6x14-3

Living
13-0x14-3

Up

Porch

60'-6"

SPECIAL FEATURES

2,009 total square feet of living area

Enter this home and find a large family room featuring a fireplace flanked by double windows

Cheerful breakfast area has access to the skylighted porch

Elegant dining area includes a built-in china cabinet

Optional bonus room above the garage has an additional 332 square feet of living area

3 bedrooms, 2 1/2 baths, 2-car side entry garage

Basement foundation

Second Floor
489 sq. ft.

Br. #2
11 x 12
8' Ceiling

Br. #3
11 x 10/7
8' Ceiling

Stairs Down

Ledge

Attic Storage

Opt. Bonus
12 x 21/5

Roof

Skylight

Roof

Master
13/8 x 15
Recessed Ceiling

Family Room
19/8 x 15
12' Ceiling

Skylight

Porch
21/8 x 6/6

Breakfast
11 x 12
9' Ceiling

Kitchen
10 x 12

Foyer
8/5 x 6/6
12' Ceiling

Dining
11 x 13
9' Ceiling
China Cab

Stoop

Desk

Stairs Up

Stairs Down

Ledge

Utility

W D

Storage
9/6 x 6/3

Garage
22 x 22

Width: 57'-0"
Depth: 61'-6"

© Copyright by
designer/architect

First Floor
1,520 sq. ft.

SPECIAL FEATURES

2,838 total square feet of living area

Energy efficient home with
2" x 6" exterior walls

10' ceilings throughout the first floor

Dining room is enhanced with
large corner bay windows

Master bath boasts a double-bowl
vanity and an oversized tub

Kitchen features an island and double sink
which overlooks the dinette and family room

4 bedrooms, 2 1/2 baths, 3-car garage

Basement foundation

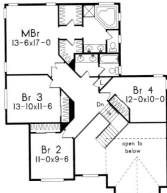

Second Floor
1,236 sq. ft.

MBr
13-6x17-0

Br 3
13-10x11-6

Br 4
12-0x10-0

Dn

Br 2
11-0x9-6

open to
below

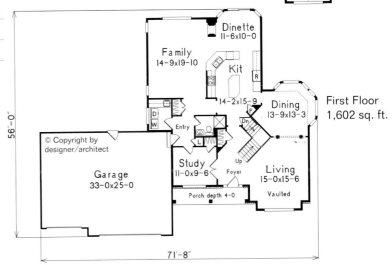

Dinette
11-6x10-0

Family
14-9x19-10

Kit

14-2x15-9

R

Dining
13-9x13-3

First Floor
1,602 sq. ft.

D
W

Entry

Study
11-0x9-6

Dn

Up

Living
15-0x15-6

Foyer

Garage
33-0x25-0

© Copyright by
designer/architect

Porch depth 4-0

Vaulted

56'-0"

71'-8"

SPECIAL FEATURES

3,164 total square feet of living area

Double-door front entry leads into the central living area with unique curved walls

Family room features a two-story ceiling, corner fireplace and built-in media center

Master bedroom accesses a covered patio

A double-door entry leads into the master bath with a large walk-in closet

Varied ceiling heights throughout

4 bedrooms, 4 baths, 3-car side entry garage

Slab foundation

First Floor
2,624 sq. ft.

Second Floor
540 sq. ft.

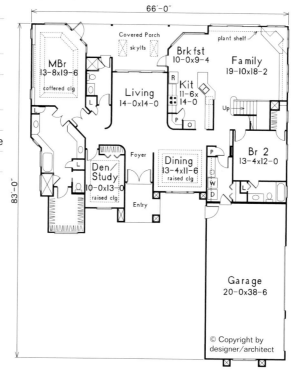

66'-0"

83'-0"

MBr
13-8x19-6
coffered clg

Living
14-0x14-0

Covered Porch
skylts

Brk fst
10-0x9-4

Kit
11-6x
14-0

Family
19-10x18-2

Up

Foyer

Dining
13-4x11-6
raised clg

Br 2
13-4x12-0

Den/
Study
10-0x13-0
raised clg.

Entry

Garage
20-0x38-6

plant shelf

open to below

Dn

Br 3
13-4x11-0

Br 4
11-0x12-4

SPECIAL FEATURES

2,587 total square feet of living area

High windows above French doors in the great room create a spectacular view

The spacious kitchen serves the breakfast and dining rooms with ease

The second floor offers plenty of space with three bedrooms and a storage area

4 bedrooms, 3 1/2 baths, 2-car side entry garage

Basement foundation

Second Floor
797 sq. ft.

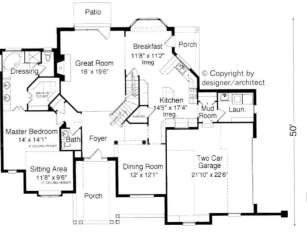

© Copyright by designer/architect

First Floor
1,790 sq. ft.

SPECIAL FEATURES

2,767 total square feet of living area

The huge great room enjoys a fireplace and vaulted ceiling

The kitchen is second-to-none including a wrap-around snack bar and walk-in corner pantry

Flanked by large covered patios, the breakfast room is drenched by sunlight through a wall of windows

The master bedroom offers an incredible bath that showcases a shower surrounded by a private garden

3 bedrooms, 3 baths, 3-car side entry garage

Crawl space foundation, drawings also include slab and basement foundations

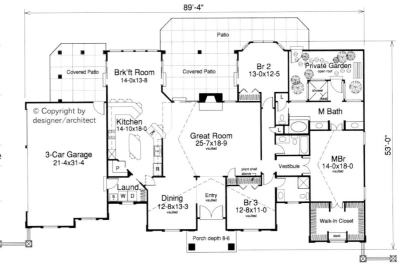

89'-4"

Patio

Covered Patio

Brk'ft Room
14-0x13-8

Covered Patio

Br 2
13-0x12-5

Private Garden
open roof

shower

M Bath

© Copyright by designer/architect

Kitchen
14-10x18-0

Great Room
25-7x18-9
vaulted

3-Car Garage
21-4x31-4

plant shelf
above

Vestibule

MBr
14-0x18-0
vaulted

53'-0"

Laund.

S W D

Dining
12-8x13-3
vaulted

Entry
vaulted

Br 3
12-8x11-0
vaulted

Walk-In Closet

desk

Porch depth 8-6

Legacy SERIES

SPECIAL FEATURES

3,019 total square feet of living area

Energy efficient home with
2" x 6" exterior walls

Master bedroom features a double-door
entry, dramatic vaulted ceiling and spacious
master bath with large bay window

Bonus room on the second floor, which is
included in the square footage, is accented
by dormer windows and ceiling vaults

Handy additional storage in
the secondary bath

4 bedrooms, 2 1/2 baths,
3-car side entry garage

Basement foundation

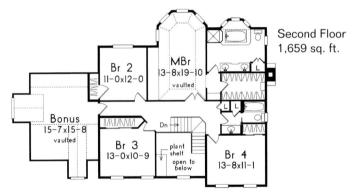

Second Floor
1,659 sq. ft.

Br 2 11-0x12-0
MBr 13-8x19-10 vaulted
Bonus 15-7x15-8 vaulted
Br 3 13-0x10-9
plant shelf open to below
Br 4 13-8x11-1
Dn

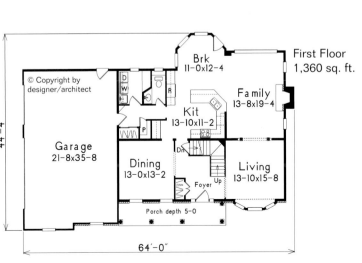

First Floor
1,360 sq. ft.

© Copyright by designer/architect

Garage 21-8x35-8

Brk 11-0x12-4
Family 13-8x19-4
Kit 13-10x11-2
Dining 13-0x13-2
Living 13-10x15-8
Foyer
Up
Dn
P
R

44'-4"
64'-0"
Porch depth 5-0

SPECIAL FEATURES

1,991 total square feet of living area

Two-story great room maintains an elegant feel with a vaulted ceiling and large fireplace

The master bedroom vaults to 12' and is brightened by a large 6' palladian window

The optional bonus suite has an additional 252 square feet of living area

3 bedrooms, 2 1/2 baths, 3-car side entry garage

Basement foundation, drawings also include crawl space foundation

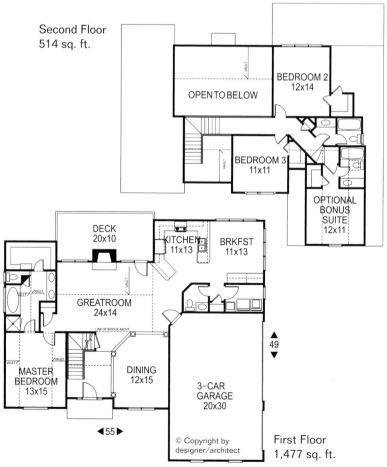

Second Floor
514 sq. ft.

OPEN TO BELOW

BEDROOM 2
12x14

BEDROOM 3
11x11

OPTIONAL BONUS SUITE
12x11

DECK
20x10

KITCHEN
11x13

BRKFST
11x13

GREATROOM
24x14

LINE OF BRIDGE ABOVE

MASTER BEDROOM
13x15

DINING
12x15

3-CAR GARAGE
20x30

49

55

© Copyright by designer/architect

First Floor
1,477 sq. ft.

SPECIAL FEATURES

2,356 total square feet of living area

Master bedroom is located on the first floor and features lots of closet space and a luxury bath

Plenty of extras throughout including a planning desk, large pantry, wet bar and a two-story great room

Second floor boasts three bedrooms and a lovely view to the great room below

4 bedrooms, 2 1/2 baths, 2-car garage

Basement foundation

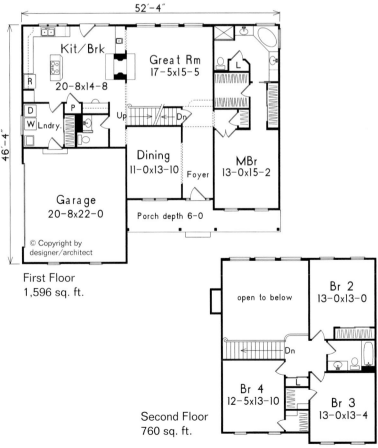

52'-4"

46'-4"

Kit/Brk
20-8x14-8

Great Rm
17-5x15-5

R

D
W Lndry.

P

Up

Dn

MBr
13-0x15-2

Dining
11-0x13-10

Foyer

Garage
20-8x22-0

Porch depth 6-0

© Copyright by designer/architect

First Floor
1,596 sq. ft.

open to below

Br 2
13-0x13-0

Dn

Br 4
12-5x13-10

Br 3
13-0x13-4

Second Floor
760 sq. ft.

SPECIAL FEATURES

2,498 total square feet of living area

Main rooms of this Colonial style home are oriented to the rear of the house

Bay windows can be found in the dining room, breakfast nook, master bedroom and bath

Bonus room above the garage, which is included in the square footage, has many possibilities and offers a generous storage area

Oversized laundry and pantry are conveniently located

Luxurious master bath and dressing area

3 bedrooms, 2 1/2 baths, 2-car garage

Crawl space foundation

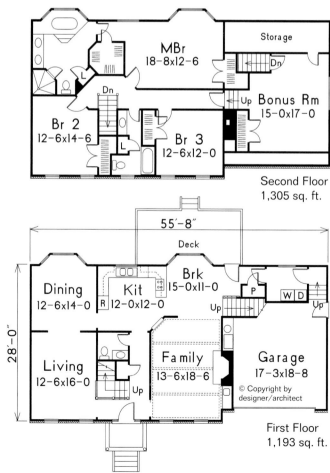

MBr
18-8x12-6

Storage

Br 2
12-6x14-6

Br 3
12-6x12-0

Bonus Rm
15-0x17-0

Dn

Up

Second Floor
1,305 sq. ft.

55'-8"

Deck

Dining
12-6x14-0

Kit
12-0x12-0

Brk
15-0x11-0

P

W D

28'-0"

Living
12-6x16-0

Family
13-6x18-6

Garage
17-3x18-8

Up

© Copyright by
designer/architect

First Floor
1,193 sq. ft.

SPECIAL FEATURES

2,148 total square feet of living area

Cheerful bayed sunroom has an attached porch and overlooks the kitchen and breakfast area

Varied ceiling heights throughout the entire plan

All bedrooms have walk-in closets

Laundry area includes handy sink

Optional bonus room on the second floor has an additional 336 square feet of living area

3 bedrooms, 2 1/2 baths, 2-car side entry garage

Basement foundation

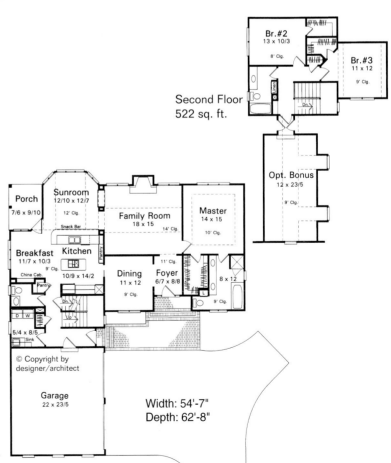

Second Floor
522 sq. ft.

Br.#2
13 x 10/3
8' Clg.

Br.#3
11 x 12
9' Clg.

Opt. Bonus
12 x 23/5
9' Clg.

Porch
7/6 x 9/10

Sunroom
12/10 x 12/7
12' Clg.

Snack Bar

Breakfast
11/7 x 10/3
9' Clg.

China Cab.

Pantry

Kitchen
10/9 x 14/2

Pantry

Family Room
18 x 15
14' Clg.

Master
14 x 15
10' Clg.

11' Clg.

Dining
11 x 12
9' Clg.

Foyer
6/7 x 8/8

8 x 12
9' Clg.

D W

Sink

5/4 x 8/5

© Copyright by
designer/architect

Garage
22 x 23/5

Width: 54'-7"
Depth: 62'-8"

First Floor
1,626 sq. ft.

SPECIAL FEATURES

3,978 total square feet of living area

Stately wood columns and mouldings dress the arched openings that separate the entry, living and dining rooms

The huge vaulted great room offers a fireplace and ascending wood-crafted staircase with balcony overlook

The spacious kitchen and breakfast room adjoin a functional mud room with rear stairs to the second floor

The bonus room on the second floor is included in the square footage

4 bedrooms, 3 full baths, 2 half baths, 3-car side entry garage

Basement foundation

Attic

Vaulted Great Room Below

Attic

Bonus Rm
19-10x17-4

Sloped Ceiling

Br 2
13-0x17-3

Br 3
13-0x13-7

Br 4
13-5x13-3

Second Floor
1,541 sq. ft.

76'-4"

Patio

48'-0"

Brk fst
13-5x9-0

W D

Laundry

Pantry

Mud Rm.

Freezer

Great Room
20-8x21-0
vaulted

Kitchen
13-5x16-10

Garage
23-4x29-4

MBr
14-4x21-0

Entry

Living Rm
13-7x17-7

Dining
12-8x15-0

© Copyright by designer/architect

Porch

First Floor
2,437 sq. ft.

SPECIAL FEATURES

2,459 total square feet of living area

Kitchen has an open feel with angled counter to enjoy views through family and breakfast rooms

Secluded master bedroom includes dressing area, access to the outdoors and private bath with tub and shower

Stylish, open stairway overlooks two-story foyer

Energy efficient home with 2" x 6" exterior walls

4 bedrooms, 2 1/2 baths, 2-car garage

Basement foundation

Second Floor
598 sq. ft.

Br 4
10-3x10-10

Br 3
10-0x10-8

Dn

Br 2
11-4x13-4

open to
below

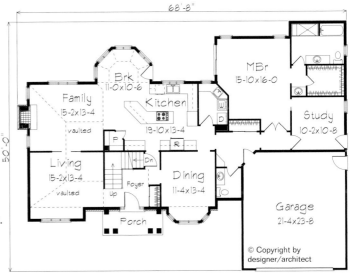

First Floor
1,861 sq. ft.

68'-8"

50'-0"

Brk
11-0x10-6

Family
15-2x13-4
vaulted

Kitchen
19-10x13-4

MBr
15-10x16-0

Study
10-2x10-8

P

Dn

Living
15-2x13-4
vaulted

Foyer

up

Dining
11-4x13-4

Garage
21-4x23-8

Porch

© Copyright by
designer/architect

LEGACY
SERIES

SPECIAL FEATURES

2,153 total square feet of living area

Foyer leads directly into the formal
living room that accesses the porch

Master bedroom features a wall of
windows and also accesses the porch

Family room boasts a 12' barrel vaulted
ceiling and built-in bookshelves on
each side of the dramatic fireplace

Varied ceiling heights throughout

Three bedrooms, a bath and the utility
room are located off the family room

4 bedrooms, 2 baths, 2-car garage

Slab foundation

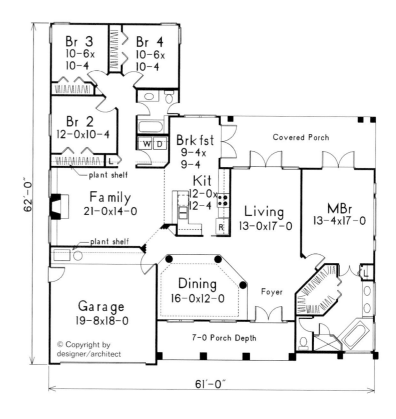

Br 3
10-6x
10-4

Br 4
10-6x
10-4

Br 2
12-0x10-4

plant shelf

Family
21-0x14-0

plant shelf

Garage
19-8x18-0

© Copyright by
designer/architect

Brk fst
9-4x
9-4

W D

Kit
12-0x
12-4

R

Dining
16-0x12-0

Living
13-0x17-0

Covered Porch

MBr
13-4x17-0

Foyer

62'-0"

61'-0"

7-0 Porch Depth

SPECIAL FEATURES

2,826 total square feet of living area

9' ceilings throughout

Fully appointed master bedroom
has a luxurious bath

Second floor bedrooms include private
dressing areas and walk-in closets

Large, well-planned kitchen
features a center island

4 bedrooms, 3 1/2 baths,
2-car side entry garage

Slab foundation, drawings also
include crawl space foundation

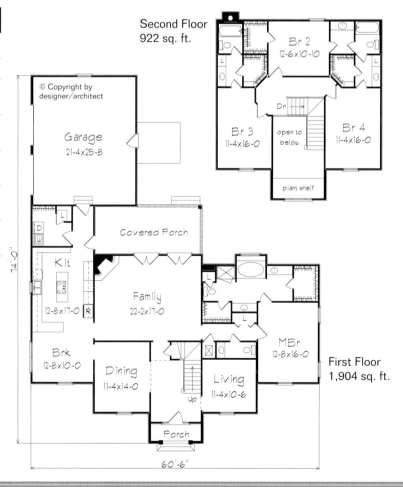

Second Floor
922 sq. ft.

First Floor
1,904 sq. ft.

SPECIAL FEATURES

2,195 total square feet of living area

Striking facade provided by gracious two-story window treatment

Bay windows add light and space

Open family and kitchen/breakfast area exit onto the spacious rear deck

4 bedrooms, 2 1/2 baths, 2-car drive under side entry garage

Basement foundation

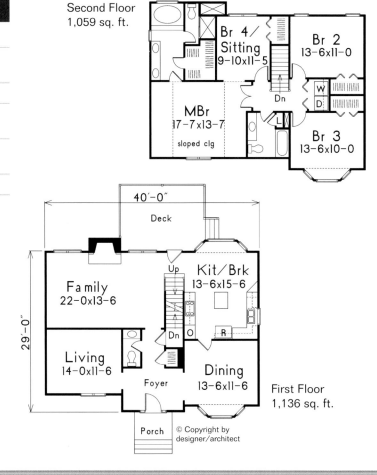

Second Floor
1,059 sq. ft.

Br 4/ Sitting
9-10x11-5

Br 2
13-6x11-0

MBr
17-7x13-7
sloped clg

Dn

W
D

Br 3
13-6x10-0

40'-0"

Deck

Up

Kit/Brk
13-6x15-6

Family
22-0x13-6

29'-0"

Dn

O

R

Living
14-0x11-6

Dining
13-6x11-6

Foyer

First Floor
1,136 sq. ft.

Porch

© Copyright by designer/architect

SPECIAL FEATURES

4,465 total square feet of living area

Brickwork and randomly placed stone, multiple gables, hip roofs, and board and batten shutters all contribute to this classic exterior

The welcoming entry takes you into the great room with views of the rear deck, a dining room with tray ceiling and a vaulted study with arched window

A well-equipped kitchen opens to the bayed breakfast room and the vaulted hearth room

The second floor enjoys a spacious media room along with three huge bedrooms

4 bedrooms, 3 1/2 baths, 3-car side entry garage

Walk-out basement foundation

Br #2
13-1x17-0

Media Room
18-1x20-8

Br #3
13-9x13-2

Hall

Br #4
20-0x12-8

Second Floor
1,648 sq. ft.

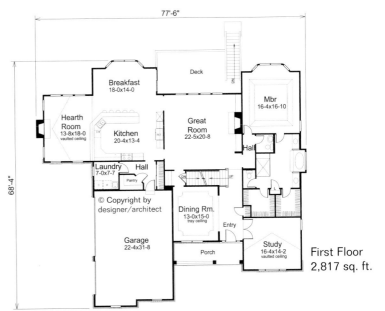

77'-6"

Breakfast
18-0x14-0

Deck

Mbr
16-4x16-10

Hearth Room
13-8x18-0
vaulted ceiling

Kitchen
20-4x13-4

Great Room
22-5x20-8

Hall

Laundry
7-0x7-7

Hall

Pantry

© Copyright by designer/architect

Dining Rm.
13-0x15-0
tray ceiling

Entry

68'-4"

Garage
22-4x31-8

Porch

Study
16-4x14-2
vaulted ceiling

First Floor
2,817 sq. ft.

LEGACY SERIES

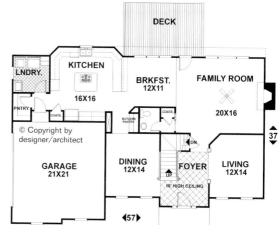

SPECIAL FEATURES

2,897 total square feet of living area

The spacious family room has a fireplace and access to the deck

The kitchen has plenty of cabinets and counterspace as well as a cooktop island

The luxurious master bath features a 6' whirlpool tub in addition to the large shower

4 bedrooms, 3 1/2 baths, 2-car side entry garage

Walk-out basement foundation

Second Floor
1,430 sq. ft.

MASTER BDRM.
OPTIONAL 36"
FIREPLACE 15X17
TRAY CEILING

BEDROOM 3
12X12

LINEN

VAULT

VAULT

LINEN

K/S

BEDROOM 2
12X14

DN

BEDROOM 4
12X13

TRAY CEILING

DECK

LNDRY

KITCHEN
16X16

BRKFST.
12X11

FAMILY ROOM
20X16

PNTRY

COATS

BUTLERS
PANTRY

COATS

37

© Copyright by designer/architect

GARAGE
21X21

DINING
12X14

FOYER

UP

18' HIGH CEILING

DN

LIVING
12X14

First Floor
1,467 sq. ft.

57

SPECIAL FEATURES

3,315 total square feet of living area

Energy efficient home with
2" x 6" exterior walls

Island kitchen, breakfast room and
two-story sunken family room combine for
convenient family dining or entertaining

Two-story foyer opens into bayed
formal dining and living rooms

Master bedroom features a sitting area,
large walk-in closet and deluxe bath

4 bedrooms, 3 1/2 baths,
2-car side entry garage

Basement foundation

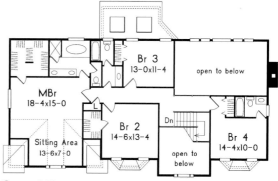

Br 3
13-0x11-4

open to below

MBr
18-4x15-0

Br 2
14-6x13-4

Dn

Br 4
14-4x10-0

Sitting Area
13-6x7-0

open to
below

Second Floor
1,620 sq. ft.

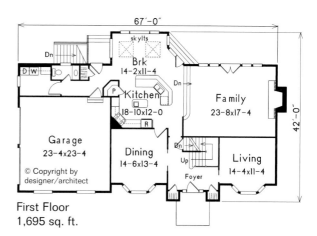

67'-0"

skylts

Dn

Brk
14-2x11-4

Dn

D W

Family
23-8x17-4

P

Kitchen
18-10x12-0

R

42'-0"

Garage
23-4x23-4

Dn

Dining
14-6x13-4

Up

Living
14-4x11-4

© Copyright by
designer/architect

Foyer

First Floor
1,695 sq. ft.

LEGACY
SERIES

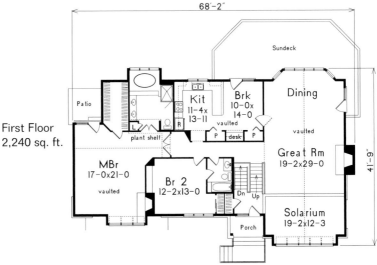

SPECIAL FEATURES

3,510 total square feet of living area

Energy efficient home with
2" x 6" exterior walls

Great room has open solarium with
balcony, greenhouse window, bay
window, stone fireplace and vaulted
ceiling creating a magical ambiance

Master bedroom boasts a sitting
area with fireplace and luxury
bath with private courtyard, both
featuring greenhouse windows

Lower level features a solarium,
large recreation area with fireplace,
walk-in bar, bedroom #3 with
bath and large laundry area

3 bedrooms, 3 baths,
2-car drive under garage

Walk-out basement foundation

First Floor
2,240 sq. ft.

68'-2"

Sundeck

Patio

Kit
11-4x
13-11

Brk
10-0x
14-0
vaulted

Dining
vaulted

plant shelf

P   desk   P

Great Rm
19-2x29-0

MBr
17-0x21-0
vaulted

Br 2
12-2x13-0

Dn Up

Solarium
19-2x12-3

Porch

41'-9"

Lower Level
1,270 sq. ft.

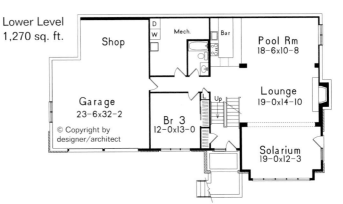

Shop

D
W

Mech.

Bar

Pool Rm
18-6x10-8

Garage
23-6x32-2

© Copyright by
designer/architect

Br 3
12-0x13-0

L Up

Lounge
19-0x14-10

Solarium
19-0x12-3

SPECIAL FEATURES

2,408 total square feet of living area

Large vaulted great room overlooks atrium and window wall, adjoins dining room, spacious breakfast room with bay and pass-through kitchen

A special private bedroom with bath, separate from other bedrooms, is perfect for a mother-in-law suite or children home from college

Atrium opens to 1,100 square feet of optional living area below

4 bedrooms, 3 baths, 3-car side entry garage

Walk-out basement foundation

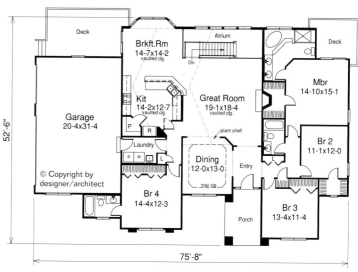

Deck

Brkft.Rm
14-7x14-2
vaulted clg.

Atrium

Dn

Garage
20-4x31-4

Kit
14-2x12-7
vaulted clg.

P

R

Great Room
19-1x18-4
vaulted clg.

Mbr
14-10x15-1

Deck

© Copyright by designer/architect

Laundry

D W L

plant shelf

Dining
12-0x13-0
tray clg.

Entry

Br 2
11-1x12-0

Br 4
14-4x12-3

Porch

Br 3
13-4x11-4

52'-6"

75'-8"

First Floor
2,408 sq. ft.

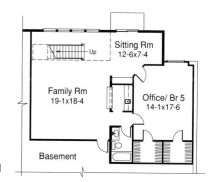

Up

Sitting Rm
12-6x7-4

Family Rm
19-1x18-4

Office/ Br 5
14-1x17-6

Optional
Lower Level

Basement

SPECIAL FEATURES

3,003 total square feet of living area

Energy efficient home with
2" x 6" exterior walls

Vaulted master bedroom features a large
walk-in closet, spa tub, separate shower
room and access to the rear patio

Covered entrance opens into the
foyer with a large greeting area

Formal living room has a 12' ceiling
and 36" walls on two sides

Island kitchen features a
large pantry and nook

Cozy fireplace accents the vaulted family
room that opens onto a covered deck

Utility room with generous space
is adjacent to a half bath

3 bedrooms, 2 1/2 baths, 3-car garage

Crawl space foundation

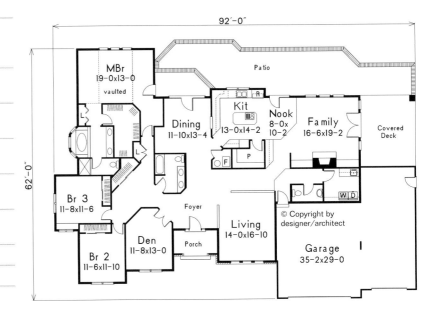

92'-0"

62'-0"

MBr
19-0x13-0
vaulted

Patio

Kit

Nook
8-0x
10-2

Family
16-6x19-2

Covered
Deck

Dining
11-10x13-4

R

F

P

Br 3
11-8x11-6

Foyer

Living
14-0x16-10

© Copyright by
designer/architect

W D

Br 2
11-6x11-10

Den
11-8x13-0

Porch

Garage
35-2x29-0

SPECIAL FEATURES

3,290 total square feet of living area

Energy efficient home with
2" x 6" exterior walls

Patio area surrounds the pool with a
swim-up bar; both the pool and spa
are great options with this plan

Formal dining room features a dramatic drop
down ceiling and easy access to the kitchen

Fireplace provides a focal point in the
master bedroom that includes a sitting
room and elegant master bath

An observation room and two
bedrooms with adjoining bath are
located on the second floor

Varied ceiling heights throughout

4 bedrooms, 3 1/2 baths,
2-car side entry garage

Slab foundation

Second Floor
621 sq. ft.

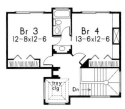

First Floor
2,669 sq. ft.

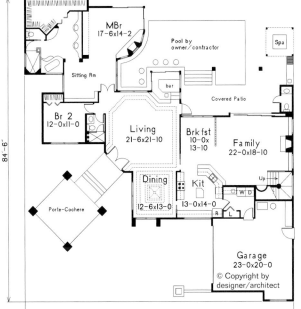

© Copyright by
designer/architect

SPECIAL FEATURES

2,764 total square feet of living area

The eye-catching exterior features brick and stone, multiple gables, a cozy porch with railing and rough cedar shake siding

A grand-sized entry accesses a private parlor with double glass doors, dining room with tray ceiling and a powder room

The kitchen enjoys a center island, huge walk-in pantry, built-in double oven and features a 50' vista through the breakfast and family rooms

A vaulted master bedroom with plush bath and two walk-in closets shares the second floor with three additional bedrooms and a Jack and Jill bath

4 bedrooms, 2 1/2 baths, 2-car garage

Basement foundation

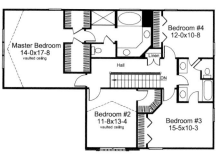

Master Bedroom
14-0x17-8
vaulted ceiling

Bedroom #4
12-0x10-8

Linen

Hall

Bedroom #2
11-8x13-4
vaulted ceiling

Bedroom #3
15-5x10-3

Second Floor
1,332 sq. ft.

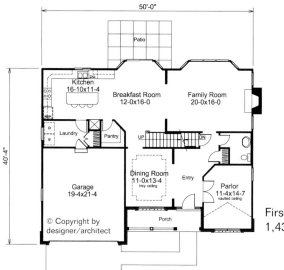

50'-0"

40'-4"

Patio

Kitchen
16-10x11-4

Breakfast Room
12-0x16-0

Family Room
20-0x16-0

Laundry

Pantry

UP

DN

Garage
19-4x21-4

Dining Room
11-0x13-4
tray ceiling

Entry

Parlor
11-4x14-7
vaulted ceiling

© Copyright by
designer/architect

Porch

First Floor
1,432 sq. ft.

SPECIAL FEATURES

2,397 total square feet of living area

A grand entry porch leads to a dramatic vaulted entry foyer with plant shelf open to the great room

The great room enjoys a 12' vaulted ceiling, atrium featuring 2 1/2 story windows and fireplace with flanking bookshelves

A conveniently located sunroom and side porch adjoin the breakfast room and garage

898 square feet of optional living area on the lower level with family room, bedroom #4 and bath

2" x 6" exterior walls available, please order plan #536-007E-0098

3 bedrooms, 2 baths, 3-car side entry garage

Walk-out basement foundation

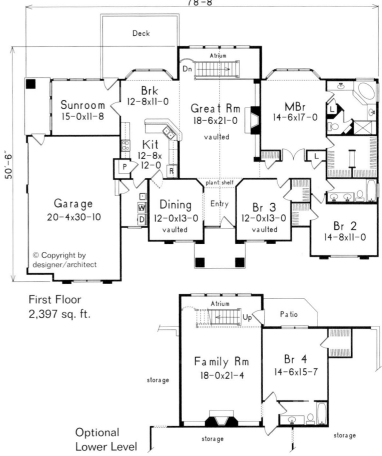

78'-8"

50'-6"

Deck

Atrium
Dn

Brk
12-8x11-0

Great Rm
18-6x21-0
vaulted

MBr
14-6x17-0

Sunroom
15-0x11-8

Kit
12-8x
12-0

Garage
20-4x30-10

Dining
12-0x13-0
vaulted

plant shelf

Entry

Br 3
12-0x13-0
vaulted

Br 2
14-8x11-0

© Copyright by designer/architect

First Floor
2,397 sq. ft.

Atrium   Up   Patio

Family Rm
18-0x21-4

Br 4
14-6x15-7

storage

Optional
Lower Level

storage

storage

LEGACY SERIES

SPECIAL FEATURES

3,169 total square feet of living area

9' ceilings throughout first floor

Second floor bedrooms boast private baths

Spacious game room includes deck/balcony

Master bedroom features a
private patio and ideal bath

4 bedrooms, 4 baths, 2-car side entry garage

Slab foundation, drawings also
include crawl space foundation

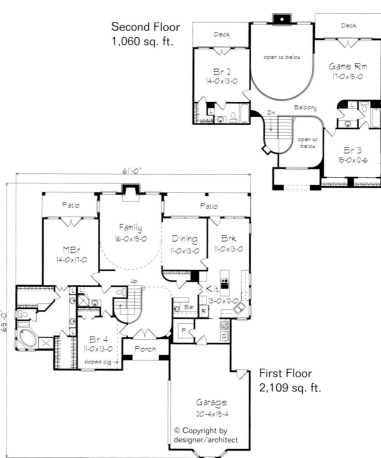

Second Floor
1,060 sq. ft.

Deck

Deck

open to below

Br 2
14-0x13-0

Game Rm
17-0x15-0

Balcony

Dn

open to below

Br 3
15-0x12-6

61'-0"

69'-0"

Patio

Patio

Family
16-0x19-0

Dining
11-0x13-0

Brk
11-0x13-0

MBr
14-0x17-0

up

Kit
13-0x12-0

Bar

Br 4
11-0x13-0

Porch

sloped clg

First Floor
2,109 sq. ft.

Garage
20-4x19-4

© Copyright by
designer/architect

SPECIAL FEATURES

2,343 total square feet of living area

Energy efficient home with
2" x 6" exterior walls

The spacious kitchen offers an
abundance of counterspace including
an extra-large center island

A butler's pantry is located
outside the formal dining room
to assist with entertaining

The airy living room features a
cathedral ceiling and grand fireplace

All bedrooms are located on the
second floor for privacy

4 bedrooms, 2 1/2 baths, 3-car garage

Basement foundation

Second Floor
1,166 sq. ft.

First Floor
1,177 sq. ft.

© Copyright by
designer/architect

SPECIAL FEATURES

2,406 total square feet of living area

Master bedroom has a beautiful fireplace, private balcony, enormous walk-in closet and private bath with dressing area

Unique kitchen-in-a-bay attaches to the breakfast area and beyond to the formal dining area that has a covered porch and fireplace

First floor activity area has a see-through fireplace, bookcases and covered veranda nearby

3 bedrooms, 2 1/2 baths

Basement foundation

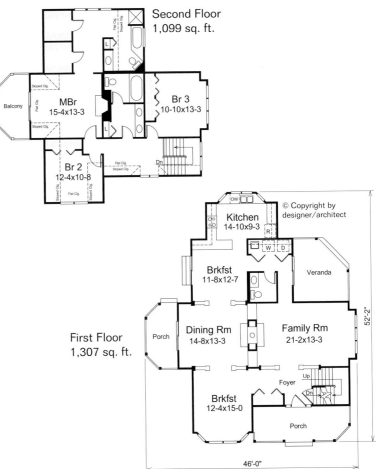

Second Floor
1,099 sq. ft.

Balcony

MBr
15-4x13-3

Br 3
10-10x13-3

Br 2
12-4x10-8

Dn

Kitchen
14-10x9-3

© Copyright by designer/architect

Brkfst
11-8x12-7

Veranda

Porch

Dining Rm
14-8x13-3

Family Rm
21-2x13-3

First Floor
1,307 sq. ft.

Foyer

Up

Dn

Brkfst
12-4x15-0

Porch

52'-2"

46'-0"

SPECIAL FEATURES

3,782 total square feet of living area

Stylish staircase in the foyer ascends to the second floor balcony overlooking the great room below

Lower level includes a media room with built-in cabinets, fireplace and ceiling mounted projector and screen

The formal dining room is decorated with an impressive tray ceiling drawing the eye upward

Massive 42" direct vent fireplace and expansive window wall helps bring the outdoors into the vaulted great room

4 bedrooms, 3 1/2 baths, 2-car garage

Basement foundation

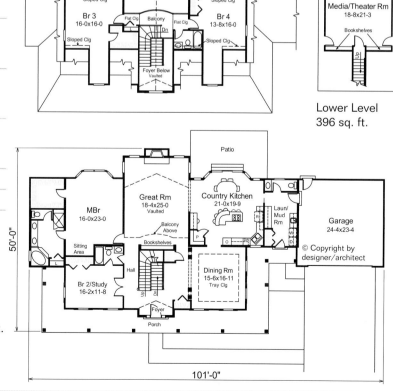

Second Floor
815 sq. ft.

Lower Level
396 sq. ft.

First Floor
2,571 sq. ft.

© Copyright by designer/architect

SPECIAL FEATURES

3,528 total square feet of living area

Two sets of windows brighten the great room while another wall contains a fireplace flanked by built-in bookshelves

Double walk-in closets flank the entry of the master bath from the bedroom

A beautiful octagon-shaped study enjoys sunlight filtering in from all directions

4 bedrooms, 3 1/2 baths,
3-car side entry garage

Basement foundation

Second Floor
1,233 sq. ft.

Second Floor

- Open To Below
- Br 2 16-10x11-10
- Br 3 13-6x12-0
- Br 4 20-10x11-1

First Floor

61'-8"
65'-8"

- MBr 14-10x16-6
- Great Room 19-10x17-10
- Brkfst/Kit 18-11x17-10
- Cov. Porch
- Dining 12-4x17-1
- Study 11-3x14-2
- Cov. Porch
- 3 Car Garage 20-8x34-0

© Copyright by
designer/architect

First Floor
2,295 sq. ft.

SPECIAL FEATURES

6,088 total square feet of living area

The two-story foyer invites you into the grand scale great room featuring a two-story stone fireplace, flanking bookshelves and window wall

Amenities galore are found in the huge kitchen including a 9' island with seating, octagonal breakfast area, vaulted hearth room with fireplace and covered porch

The master bedroom offers a bay window, coffered ceiling and colossal bath with sauna, whirlpool tub and two enormous walk-in closets

The garage with large storage room includes an adjacent office with private entrance, half bath and patio

Three bedrooms, each with their own bath and walk-in closet, a dramatic balcony overlooking the great room and private staircase to the kitchen are features of the second floor

4 bedrooms, 4 full baths, 2 half baths, 5-car side entry garage

Basement foundation

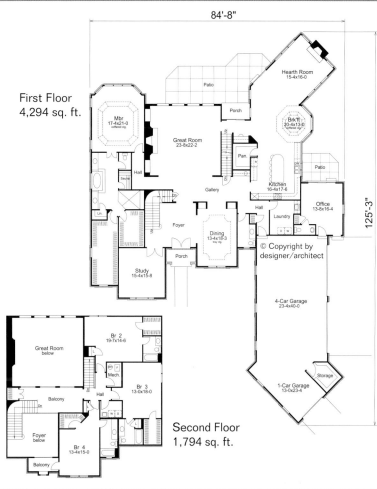

First Floor
4,294 sq. ft.

Second Floor
1,794 sq. ft.

© Copyright by designer/architect

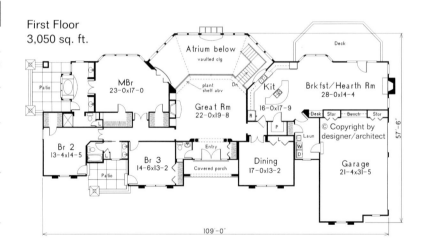

SPECIAL FEATURES

4,826 total square feet of living area

Brightly lit entry connects to great room with balcony and massive bay-shaped atrium

Kitchen has island/snack bar, walk-in pantry, computer area and an atrium overlook

Master bedroom has a sitting area, walk-in closets, atrium overlook and luxury bath with private courtyard

Family room/atrium, home theater area with wet bar, game room and guest bedroom comprise the lower level

4 bedrooms, 3 1/2 baths, 3-car side entry garage

Walk-out basement foundation with lawn and garden workroom

Interior View - Great Room/Atrium

First Floor
3,050 sq. ft.

Lower Level
1,776 sq. ft.

SPECIAL FEATURES

3,357 total square feet of living area

Attractive balcony overlooks
entry foyer and living area

Balcony area could easily
convert to a fifth bedroom

Spacious kitchen also opens into a
sunken family room with a fireplace

First floor master bedroom boasts a
large walk-in closet and dressing area

Central laundry room has a laundry
chute from the second floor

4 bedrooms, 2 full baths,
2 half baths, 2-car side entry garage

Basement foundation, drawings also
include crawl space and slab foundations

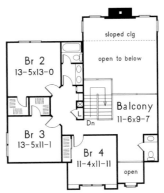

Second Floor
983 sq. ft.

sloped clg

open to below

Br 2
13-5x13-0

Balcony
11-6x9-7

Dn

Br 3
13-5x11-1

Br 4
11-4x11-11

open

First Floor
2,374 sq. ft.

69'-0"

Patio

Brk
11-5x9-3

Living
18-9x25-0

MBr
15-8x16-7

Dn

Family
14-0x22-5

W
D

Kit

P

Dn   Up

11-1x14-9

R

55'-8"

Dining
12-4x12-11

Garage
22-9x22-10

Foyer

Study
11-5x13-0

Porch

sloped clg

© Copyright by
designer/architect

SPECIAL FEATURES

2,253 total square feet of living area

Two bedrooms on the second floor share a bath

Two walk-in closets, a private bath and a sitting area leading to an outdoor deck are all amenities of the master suite

Bonus room on the second floor has an additional 247 square feet of living area

4 bedrooms, 3 baths, 2-car side entry garage

Walk-out basement foundation, drawings also include crawl space and slab foundations

Second Floor
534 sq. ft.

ATTIC STORAGE

OPEN BELOW
19'-0" x 16'-0"

BEDROOM 2
11'-0" x 14'-0"

BEDROOM 3
11'-0" x 14'-0"

BONUS ROOM
10'-4" x 22'-4"

© Copyright by designer/architect

First Floor
1,719 sq. ft.

DECK
21'-0" x 11'-4"

BREAKFAST
11'-0" x 10'-8"

HERS   HIS

SITTING
6'-6" x 7'-2"
9' HIGH CEILING

SCREENED PORCH
9'-4" x 16'-0"

11' TRAY CEILING

10' HIGH CEILING

FAMILY ROOM
19'-0" x 16'-0"

KITCHEN
11'-0" x 14'-10"

MASTER SUITE
16'-0" x 14'-0"

51'-0"

PANTRY

ENTRY
7'-8" x 16'-8"

DINING
11'-0" x 13'-0"

9' TRAY CEILING

GARAGE
20'-8" x 24'-2"

9' HIGH CEILING

STUDY/ GUEST ROOM
12'-0" x 12'-8"

PORCH
18'-2" x 5'-4"

57'-0"

3 CAR GARAGE OPTION

SPECIAL FEATURES

2,320 total square feet of living area

From the foyer, there is a panoramic view of the dramatic great room and formal dining room

A butler's pantry is strategically placed between the formal dining room and casual breakfast room

French doors add light and style to the breakfast room

4 bedrooms, 2 1/2 baths, 2-car garage

Basement foundation

Second Floor
725 sq. ft.

First Floor
1,595 sq. ft.

© Copyright by designer/architect

LEGACY SERIES

SPECIAL FEATURES

2,372 total square feet of living area

Spacious living room features an opening to the entry flanked by bookshelves

Sunken family room boasts an impressive fireplace and large window

Well-appointed kitchen includes a snack counter

Second floor bedrooms combine extravagant room sizes with lots of walk-in closets

4 bedrooms, 2 1/2 baths, 2-car garage

Basement foundation, drawings also include crawl space and slab foundations

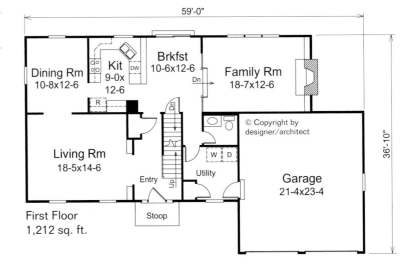

Br 4
12-0x12-6

Br 3
12-1x15-6

Br 2
11-2x12-1

MBr
12-1x18-8

Second Floor
1,160 sq. ft.

59'-0"

Dining Rm
10-8x12-6

Kit
9-0x
12-6

DW

Brkfst
10-6x12-6

Family Rm
18-7x12-6

R

Living Rm
18-5x14-6

© Copyright by
designer/architect

W D

Utility

Garage
21-4x23-4

Entry

Up

Stoop

36'-10"

First Floor
1,212 sq. ft.

SPECIAL FEATURES

2,207 total square feet of living area

The spacious great room boasts a
12' ceiling and corner fireplace

The kitchen connects to the breakfast
area and great room with an eating bar

Extra storage is located in the garage

4 bedrooms, 2 1/2 baths,
2-car side entry garage

Basement foundation, drawings also
include crawl space and slab foundations

Interior View - Great Room

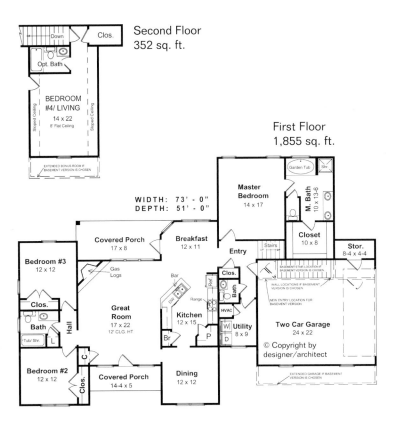

Second Floor
352 sq. ft.

Down | Clos.

Opt. Bath

BEDROOM
#4/ LIVING
14 x 22
8' Flat Ceiling

Sloped Ceiling

EXTENDED BONUS ROOM IF
BASEMENT VERSION IS CHOSEN

First Floor
1,855 sq. ft.

WIDTH: 73' - 0"
DEPTH: 51' - 0"

Garden Tub | Shr.

Master
Bedroom
14 x 17

M. Bath
10 x 13-6

Closet
10 x 8

Stor.
8-4 x 4-4

Entry

Stairs

BASEMENT STAIR LOCATION IF
BASEMENT VERSION IS CHOSEN

WALL LOCATIONS IF BASEMENT
VERSION IS CHOSEN

NEW ENTRY LOCATION FOR
BASEMENT VERSION

Covered Porch
17 x 8

Breakfast
12 x 11

Bedroom #3
12 x 12

Gas
Logs

Bar

Clos.

Clos.

Bath

Clos.

Bath

Tub/ Shr.

Hall

Great
Room
17 x 22
12' CLG. HT.

DW

Range

Ref.

Kitchen
12 x 15

HVAC

W

D

Utility
8 x 9

Two Car Garage
24 x 22

© Copyright by
designer/architect

Br

P

Bedroom #2
12 x 12

Covered Porch
14-4 x 5

Dining
12 x 12

EXTENDED GARAGE IF BASEMENT
VERSION IS CHOSEN

LEGACY SERIES

SPECIAL FEATURES

2,200 total square feet of living area

Open first floor features convenient access to the laundry area

Second floor captures space above garage for a large recreation area or future bedrooms

Oversized country kitchen has plenty of space for entertaining

Bonus room on the second floor is included in the square footage

3 bedrooms, 2 1/2 baths, 2-car garage

Basement foundation

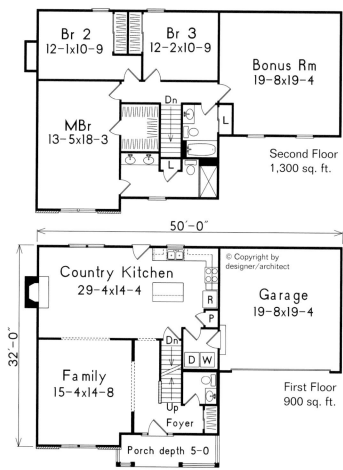

Br 2
12-1x10-9

Br 3
12-2x10-9

Bonus Rm
19-8x19-4

MBr
13-5x18-3

Dn

Second Floor
1,300 sq. ft.

50'-0"

Country Kitchen
29-4x14-4

© Copyright by
designer/architect

Garage
19-8x19-4

32'-0"

Dn

Family
15-4x14-8

Up

Foyer

First Floor
900 sq. ft.

Porch depth 5-0

SPECIAL FEATURES

3,180 total square feet of living area

Majestic exterior through use of brick has projected window and corner quoins

Two-story entry with balcony overlook leads to an extravagant U-shaped staircase built in a bay window wall

Preparing festive meals is irresistible in this kitchen and are conveniently served in a sun-drenched breakfast room

Other features include the master bedroom sitting room, bedroom #3 balcony and coffered volume ceilings in the living and dining rooms

3 bedrooms, 2 1/2 baths,
2-car side entry garage

Basement foundation

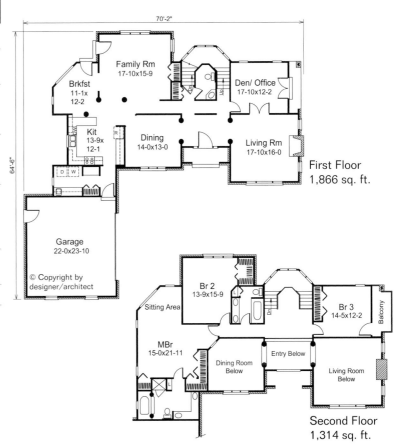

70'-2"

64'-6"

Family Rm
17-10x15-9

Brkfst
11-1x
12-2

Den/ Office
17-10x12-2

Kit
13-9x
12-1

Dining
14-0x13-0

Living Rm
17-10x16-0

First Floor
1,866 sq. ft.

Garage
22-0x23-10

© Copyright by
designer/architect

Br 2
13-9x15-9

Sitting Area

Br 3
14-5x12-2

Balcony

MBr
15-0x21-11

Dining Room
Below

Entry Below

Living Room
Below

Second Floor
1,314 sq. ft.

SPECIAL FEATURES

2,468 total square feet of living area

Open floor plan has a family room with columns, fireplace, triple French doors and a 12' ceiling

Master bath features double walk-in closets and vanities

Bonus room above garage has a private stairway and is included in the total square footage

Bedrooms are separate from the main living space for privacy

3 bedrooms, 2 1/2 baths, 2-car side entry garage

Slab foundation

63'-0"

© Copyright by designer/architect

Garage
22-0x22-0

W D

Porch

MBr
16-0x14-0

Porch

Up

Br 3
11-0x12-0

Brk
14-0x10-0

Family
20-0x17-0

Kit
10-0x
13-0

Dining
12-0x15-0

Living
12-0x12-0

Br 2
11-0x12-0

60'-4"

First Floor
2,215 sq. ft.

Bonus
12-0x22-0

Dn

Second Floor
253 sq. ft.

SPECIAL FEATURES

3,222 total square feet of living area

Two-story foyer features a central staircase and views to the second floor, dining and living rooms

Built-in breakfast booth is surrounded by windows

Gourmet kitchen includes a view to the great room

Two-story great room features a large fireplace and arched openings to the second floor

Elegant master bedroom has a separate reading room with bookshelves and fireplace

4 bedrooms, 3 1/2 baths, 2-car side entry garage

Basement foundation, drawings also include crawl space and slab foundations

Second Floor
946 sq. ft.

Br 2
12-11x12-7

open to below

Br 3
12-0x13-3

Dn

Br 4
12-1x12-4

open to below

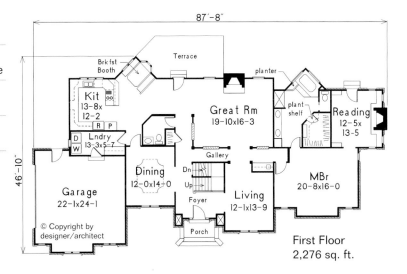

First Floor
2,276 sq. ft.

87'-8"

46'-10"

Brk fst Booth

Terrace

planter

Kit
13-8x
12-2

Great Rm
19-10x16-3

plant shelf

Reading
12-5x
13-5

R P

Lndry
13-3x5-7

D
W

Gallery

Dining
12-0x14-0

Dn
Up

Living
12-1x13-9

MBr
20-8x16-0

Garage
22-1x24-1

Foyer

Porch

© Copyright by designer/architect

SPECIAL FEATURES

2,352 total square feet of living area

Energy efficient home with
2" x 6" exterior walls

Separate family and living rooms for
casual and formal entertaining

Master bedroom with private
dressing area and bath

Bedrooms are located on the
second floor for privacy

4 bedrooms, 2 1/2 baths,
2-car rear entry garage

Crawl space foundation, drawings also
include basement and slab foundations

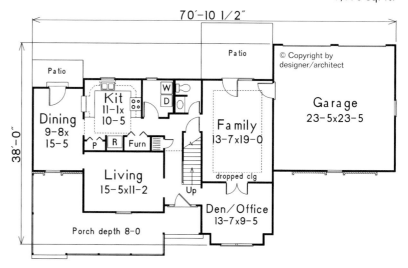

Second Floor
1,182 sq. ft.

MBr
15-2x15-5

Br 3
13-7x10-0

Br 2
15-5x10-10

Br 4
13-7x9-6

Dn

L

Porch

First Floor
1,170 sq. ft.

70'-10 1/2"

38'-0"

Patio

Patio

© Copyright by
designer/architect

Kit
11-1x
10-5

W
D

Dining
9-8x
15-5

P   R   Furn

Family
13-7x19-0

Garage
23-5x23-5

Living
15-5x11-2

Up

dropped clg

Den/Office
13-7x9-5

Porch depth 8-0

SPECIAL FEATURES

2,484 total square feet of living area

Columns and an arched opening frame the kitchen from the great room, and a box-bay window expands the breakfast area

A triple sliding glass door introduces an abundance of light and invites the activities to continue to the rear covered porch

A secondary bedroom with a private bath makes a wonderful guest room

4 bedrooms, 3 1/2 baths, 2-car side entry garage

Basement foundation

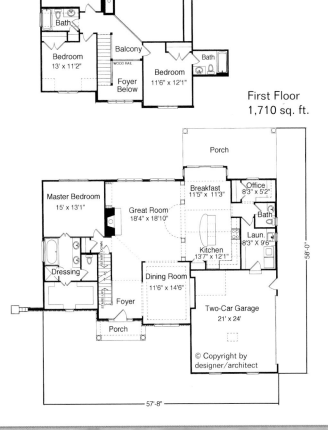

Second Floor
774 sq. ft.

Bedroom 14'2" x 11'

Great Room Below

Bath

Bedroom 13' x 11'2"

Balcony

WOOD RAIL

Foyer Below

Bedroom 11'6" x 12'1"

Bath

First Floor
1,710 sq. ft.

Porch

Master Bedroom 15' x 13'1"

Great Room 18'4" x 18'10"

Breakfast 11'5" x 11'3"

Office 8'3" x 5'2"

Bath

Kitchen 13'7" x 12'1"

Laun. 8'3" X 9'6"

Dressing

Dining Room 11'6" x 14'6"

Foyer

Two-Car Garage 21' x 24'

Porch

STAIRS UP

58'-0"

57'-8"

© Copyright by designer/architect

SPECIAL FEATURES

2,400 total square feet of living area

Use of T-stair makes efficient room travel

Large kitchen/breakfast area has planning desk, center island and a walk-in pantry

Generous closets are found in every bedroom

2" x 6" exterior walls available, please order plan #536-058D-0087

3 bedrooms, 2 1/2 baths, 3-car side entry garage

Basement foundation

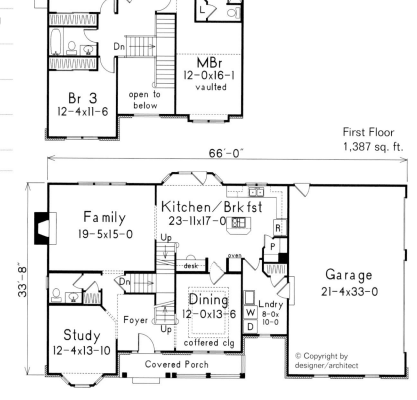

Second Floor
1,013 sq. ft.

Br 2
12-4x11-2

MBr
12-0x16-1
vaulted

Dn

open to below

Br 3
12-4x11-6

First Floor
1,387 sq. ft.

66'-0"

33'-8"

Family
19-5x15-0

Kitchen/Brkfst
23-11x17-0

Garage
21-4x33-0

Up

desk

oven

R

P

Dn

Dining
12-0x13-6

coffered clg

Lndry
8-0x
10-0

W   D

Foyer

Up

Study
12-4x13-10

Covered Porch

SPECIAL FEATURES

3,808 total square feet of living area

Cozy hearth room shares a
fireplace with the great room

See-through fireplace
connects gathering areas

Master bath features stylish angled
glass block walls that frame the
private toilet and large shower

3 bedrooms, 3 baths, 2-car garage

Walk-out basement foundation

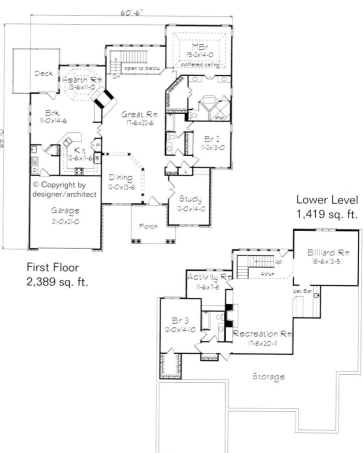

60'-6"

65'-0"

Deck

Hearth Rm
13-6x11-0

MBr
19-2x14-0
coffered ceiling

open to below

Dn

Brk
11-0x14-6

Great Rm
17-6x22-6

shwr

Kit
12-6x11-6

Br 2
11-2x13-0

© Copyright by
designer/architect

Dining
12-0x13-6

Garage
21-0x21-0

Study
12-0x14-0

Porch

First Floor
2,389 sq. ft.

Lower Level
1,419 sq. ft.

Billiard Rm
18-6x13-5

up

Atrium

Activity Rm
11-6x7-8

Wet Bar

Br 3
12-0x14-10

Recreation Rm
17-8x20-11

Storage

SPECIAL FEATURES

2,645 total square feet of living area

First floor activity area has a wall of windows creating a cheerful atmosphere

Formal living room has a box-bay window and cozy fireplace

Master bedroom and bedroom #2 have distinctive sloped ceilings

3 bedrooms, 2 1/2 baths, 2-car side entry garage

Basement foundation

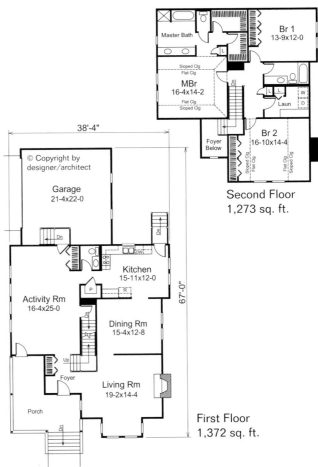

Master Bath

Br 1
13-9x12-0

Sloped Clg
Flat Clg

MBr
16-4x14-2

Flat Clg
Sloped Clg

Laun
W
D

Foyer
Below

Br 2
16-10x14-4

Sloped Clg Flat Clg   Flat Clg Sloped Clg

Second Floor
1,273 sq. ft.

38'-4"

© Copyright by
designer/architect

Garage
21-4x22-0

Dn

Dn

Kitchen
15-11x12-0

Activity Rm
16-4x25-0

P

R

DW

67'-0"

Dining Rm
15-4x12-8

Up

Foyer

Living Rm
19-2x14-4

Porch

Dn

First Floor
1,372 sq. ft.

SPECIAL FEATURES

2,343 total square feet of living area

Energy efficient home with
2" x 6" exterior walls

Beautiful fireplaces warm both the
hearth room and the family room

The covered porch can be accessed from
the hearth room through double-doors

The center island in the kitchen adds critical
workspace and dining area if needed

4 bedrooms, 2 1/2 baths, 2-car garage

Basement foundation

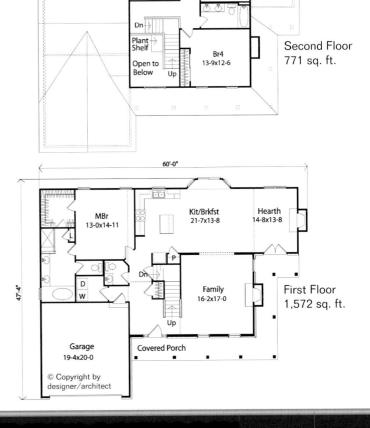

Br2
11-4x12-1

Br3
11-4x12-6

Dn
Plant
Shelf

Open to
Below   Up

Br4
13-9x12-6

Second Floor
771 sq. ft.

60'-0"

47'-4"

MBr
13-0x14-11

Kit/Brkfst
21-7x13-8

Hearth
14-8x13-8

D
W

Dn

P

Family
16-2x17-0

Up

First Floor
1,572 sq. ft.

Garage
19-4x20-0

Covered Porch

© Copyright by
designer/architect

SPECIAL FEATURES

2,993 total square feet of living area

10' ceilings on the first floor,
9' ceilings on the second floor

Second floor bedrooms
include private dressing areas,
walk-in closets and share a bath

Generous family room and kitchen
combine for an activity center

4 bedrooms, 3 baths, 2-car side entry garage

Slab foundation, drawings also
include crawl space foundation

© Copyright by
designer/architect

Garage
20-4x21-6

Br 3
13-0x11-0

open to
below

Br 4
14-0x11-0

plant
shelf

Dn

Second Floor
624 sq. ft.

Laun
7-0x14-0

Brk
12-0x14-0

skylt

MBr
15-0x14-0

Kitchen
15-0x16-0

Family
21-0x17-0

P

R

Dining
14-0x12-0

Foyer

Up

Living
12-0x12-0

Br 2
12-0x12-0

80'-0"

62'-6"

First Floor
2,369 sq. ft.

SPECIAL FEATURES

2,501 total square feet of living area

Oversized kitchen with work island, vaulted ceiling and plant shelves

An open staircase overlooks the kitchen

Secluded second floor guest bedroom features private half bath

Covered deck is accessible from the dining room and kitchen

4 bedrooms, 2 1/2 baths, 2-car side entry garage

Basement foundation, drawings also include crawl space and slab foundations

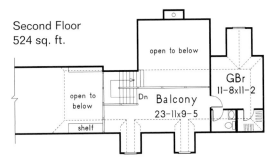

Second Floor
524 sq. ft.

open to below

GBr
11-8x11-2

open to below

Dn   Balcony
23-11x9-5

shelf

First Floor
1,977 sq. ft.

64'-0"

Patio

Covered Deck

Dining
15-2x10-8

Great Rm
16-1x24-1

MBr
14-3x13-10

47'-8"

R

Kit/Brk
19-4x14-1

Up
Dn
vaulted

P

Foyer

© Copyright by
designer/architect

D   W

Porch

Br 2
10-5x
13-0

Br 3
10-0x
13-8

Garage
23-1x22-8

LEGACY SERIES

SPECIAL FEATURES

2,024 total square feet of living area

Covered porches offer a relaxing atmosphere

Bedrooms are separated for privacy

The formal dining room provides an elegant space for entertaining

The second floor living area and optional bath are ideal for a guest suite

3 bedrooms, 2 baths, 2-car side entry garage

Basement foundation, drawings also include crawl space and slab foundations

Second Floor
386 sq. ft.

Closet

WH

Optional Bath

Living Area
14-4 x 16-6
Flat Clg.

Slope

First Floor
1,638 sq. ft.

WIDTH: 73' - 0"
DEPTH: 41' - 0"

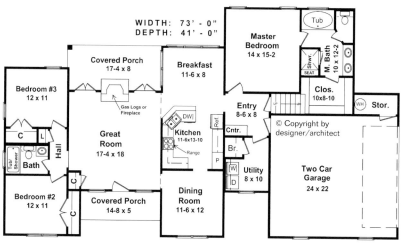

Master Bedroom
14 x 15-2

Tub

M. Bath
10 x 12-2

Shwr.
SEAT

Covered Porch
17-4 x 8

Breakfast
11-6 x 8

Clos.
10x8-10

WH Stor.

Bedroom #3
12 x 11

Gas Logs or Fireplace

Entry
8-6 x 8

© Copyright by designer/architect

C   L

Great Room
17-4 x 18

DW

Ref

Cntr.

Kitchen
11-6x13-10

Range

Br.

Two Car Garage
24 x 22

Hall

Tub/Shower

Bath

P

W
D

Utility
8 x 10

C

Bedroom #2
12 x 11

C

Covered Porch
14-8 x 5

Dining Room
11-6 x 12

SPECIAL FEATURES

3,061 total square feet of living area

Formal living and dining
rooms flank the foyer

The great room connects to the
bayed breakfast area with a bar

All bedrooms are located on the
second floor for privacy

Bonus room on second floor would
make an ideal children's play area and
is included in the square footage

4 bedrooms, 3 1/2 baths, 2-car garage

Basement foundation

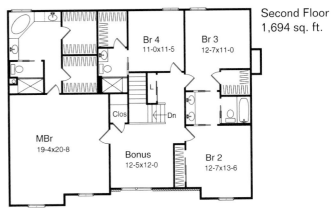

Second Floor
1,694 sq. ft.

Br 4
11-0x11-5

Br 3
12-7x11-0

Clos

L

Dn

MBr
19-4x20-8

Bonus
12-5x12-0

Br 2
12-7x13-6

First Floor
1,367 sq. ft.

48'-0"

40'-6"

Kitchen
13-3x14-3

Breakfast
13-10x12-3

Bar Top

Great Room
18-3x17-5

R

S

Pantry

W

D

Up

Dn

Garage
19-4x19-4

Dining
10-10x12-0

Living
10-3x15-5

Porch

SPECIAL FEATURES

4,269 total square feet of living area

The classic foyer with marble tile enjoys a two-story vaulted ceiling, a dramatic second floor balcony and view through a 6' x 9' elliptical window

First floor features large-sized living, dining and family rooms plus a convenient guest bedroom

Second floor master bedroom suite includes two huge walk-in closets, sitting room with bay window and luxury bath

6 bedrooms, 4 1/2 baths, 3-car side entry garage

Basement foundation

Second Floor
2,127 sq. ft.

Br 2
13-0x15-0

MBr
22-0x15-0
vaulted clg

Sitting

plant shelf

Br 5
13-7x12-0

open to below

Dn

L

Br 3
15-8x15-0

open to below
vaulted clg

Br 4
13-0x15-0

First Floor
2,142 sq. ft.

Patio

Guest
14-8x12-0

Family
22-0x15-0

Brk fst
12-8x14-4

Kit
13-0x12-4

Up

Dn

P

W D

Living
18-0x17-3

Foyer

Dining
13-0x15-0

Garage
21-4x29-4

Porch

© Copyright by designer/architect

51'-4"

64'-8"

SPECIAL FEATURES

2,900 total square feet of living area

Energy efficient home with
2" x 6" exterior walls

The grand-scale great room offers a
vaulted ceiling and palladian windows
flanking an 8' wide brick fireplace

A smartly designed built-in-a-bay kitchen
features a picture window above sink, huge
pantry, cooktop island and is open to a
large morning room with 12' of cabinetry

All bedrooms include immense closet space

1,018 square feet of optional living
area on the lower level with family room,
walk-in bar and a fifth bedroom with a bath

4 bedrooms, 2 1/2 baths,
3-car side entry garage

Walk-out basement foundation

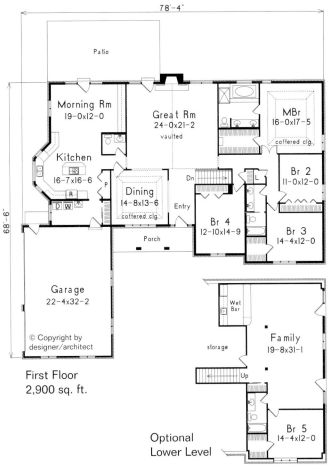

First Floor
2,900 sq. ft.

Optional
Lower Level

© Copyright by
designer/architect

LEGACY SERIES

SPECIAL FEATURES

1,736 total square feet of living area

Vaulted master bedroom features a double-door entry and private bath

Garage apartment comes complete with adjacent terrace and porch

Windows surround the cozy dining room for added sunshine

3 bedrooms, 3 baths, 2-car garage

Slab foundation

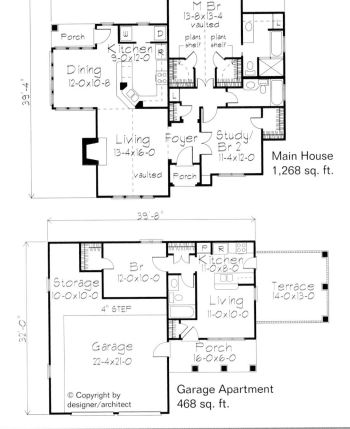

Main House
1,268 sq. ft.

44'-4"

39'-4"

Porch

Kitchen
9-0x12-0

Dining
12-0x10-8

M Br
13-8x13-4
vaulted

plant shelf   plant shelf

Living
13-4x16-0
vaulted

Foyer

Study/
Br 2
11-4x12-0

Porch

Garage Apartment
468 sq. ft.

39'-8"

32'-0"

Storage
10-0x10-0

Br
12-0x10-0

Kitchen
11-0x8-0

Terrace
14-0x13-0

Living
11-0x10-0

4" STEP

Garage
22-4x21-0

Porch
16-0x6-0

Rear View

SPECIAL FEATURES

2,353 total square feet of living area

Prominent entry highlights impressive foyer

Garage has storage/work area
and convenient laundry closet

Family room fireplace flanked by cabinets
and floor-to-ceiling bookshelves

Second floor balconies overlook
foyer and family room

4 bedrooms, 2 1/2 baths, 2-car garage

Basement foundation, drawings also
include slab and crawl space foundations

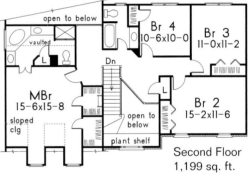

open to below

vaulted

Br 4
10-6x10-0

Br 3
11-0x11-2

Dn

L

MBr
15-6x15-8

sloped
clg

open to
below

plant shelf

Br 2
15-2x11-6

Second Floor
1,199 sq. ft.

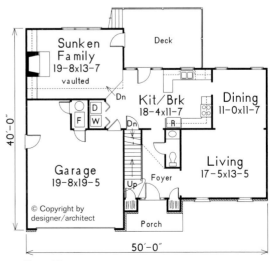

Sunken
Family
19-8x13-7
vaulted

Deck

Dn

Kit/Brk
18-4x11-7

Dining
11-0x11-7

F   D
    W

Dn

R

40'-0"

Garage
19-8x19-5

Up

Foyer

Living
17-5x13-5

© Copyright by
designer/architect

Porch

50'-0"

First Floor
1,154 sq. ft.

LEGACY SERIES

SPECIAL FEATURES

2,563 total square feet of living area

Contemporary facade with traditional flair

Impressive 13' high volume ceilings in the grand foyer and sunken living room

Breathtaking garden room with dining island features vaulted skylit ceiling, surrounding window wall and hidden whirlpool retreat off the master bedroom

Vaulted master bedroom includes view of garden and lavish bath

3 bedrooms, 2 baths, 2-car garage

Basement foundation

Interior View - Dining Room

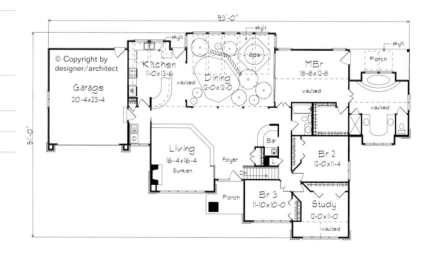

LOWE'S
LEGACY
SERIES

SPECIAL FEATURES

2,649 total square feet of living area

Energy efficient home with
2" x 6" exterior walls

A see-through fireplace warms the
kitchen, nook and family rooms

The kitchen features a cooktop island
with rounded seating and opens
into the cheerful bayed nook

Secondary bedrooms both feature
walk-in closets and share a bath

3 bedrooms, 2 1/2 baths,
3-car side entry garage

Basement foundation

Second Floor
636 sq. ft.

First Floor
2,013 sq. ft.

© Copyright by
designer/architect

LEGACY SERIES

SPECIAL FEATURES

2,517 total square feet of living area

Energy efficient home with
2" x 6" exterior walls

Central living room with large
windows and attractive transoms

Varied ceiling heights throughout home

Secluded master bedroom features
double-door entry, luxurious bath with
separate shower, step-up whirlpool tub,
double vanities and walk-in closets

Kitchen with walk-in pantry overlooks
large family room with fireplace and
unique octagon-shaped breakfast room

4 bedrooms, 2 1/2 baths, 2-car garage

Slab foundation, drawings also
include crawl space foundation

SPECIAL FEATURES

4,522 total square feet of living area

Large living room with cathedral ceiling views front terrace

Kitchen, cheery breakfast room and huge family room combine creating an exciting space

First floor master bedroom features a bath that defines luxury

A second staircase serves the second floor's three bedrooms and mammoth bonus room which is included in the total square footage

4 bedrooms, 3 1/2 baths, 2-car garage

Partial basement/crawl space foundation

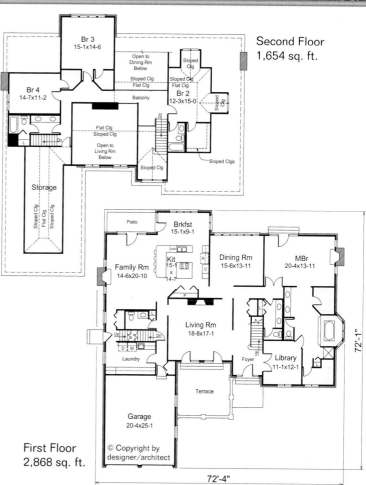

Second Floor
1,654 sq. ft.

Br 3
15-1x14-6

Open to Dining Rm Below

Sloped Clg
Flat Clg

Sloped Clg
Flat Clg

Sloped Clg

Br 4
14-7x11-2

Balcony

Br 2
12-3x15-0

Sloped Clg

Flat Clg
Sloped Clg

Open to Living Rm Below

Sloped Clgs

Sloped Clg

Storage

Sloped Clg
Flat Clg
Sloped Clg

First Floor
2,868 sq. ft.

Patio

Brkfst
15-1x9-1

Dining Rm
15-6x13-11

MBr
20-4x13-11

Kit
15-1 x 14-7

Family Rm
14-6x20-10

Living Rm
18-8x17-1

Library
11-1x12-1

Foyer

Laundry

Terrace

Garage
20-4x25-1

72'-1"

72'-4"

© Copyright by designer/architect

SPECIAL FEATURES

2,366 total square feet of living area

Foyer features a powder room, guest closet and laundry access

Convenient to the U-shaped kitchen is a dining area with sunny bay windows

All the bedrooms are located on the second floor for convenient family living

5 bedrooms, 2 1/2 baths, 2-car garage

Partial basement/crawl space foundation

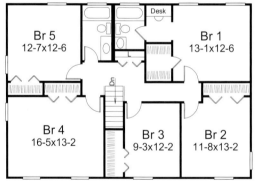

Br 5
12-7x12-6

Desk

Br 1
13-1x12-6

Dn

Br 4
16-5x13-2

Br 3
9-3x12-2

Br 2
11-8x13-2

Second Floor
1,218 sq. ft.

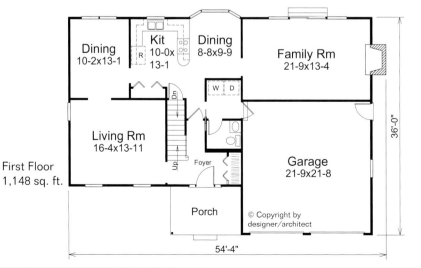

Dining
10-2x13-1

Kit
10-0x13-1

R

Dining
8-8x9-9

Family Rm
21-9x13-4

W   D

Living Rm
16-4x13-11

Dn

Up

Foyer

Garage
21-9x21-8

First Floor
1,148 sq. ft.

Porch

© Copyright by
designer/architect

36'-0"

54'-4"

SPECIAL FEATURES

2,511 total square feet of living area

Screened porch is accessible from three different living areas

Feeling of spaciousness is created by the vaulted kitchen and family area

Unfinished storage on the second floor has an additional 533 square feet of area for living or extra storage

3 bedrooms, 2 1/2 baths, 2-car side entry garage

Basement foundation, drawings also include crawl space and slab foundations

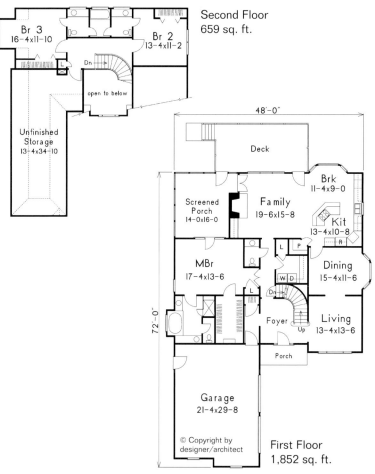

Second Floor
659 sq. ft.

Br 3
16-4x11-10

Br 2
13-4x11-2

Dn

open to below

Unfinished Storage
13-4x34-10

48'-0"

Deck

Brk
11-4x9-0

Screened Porch
14-0x16-0

Family
19-6x15-8

Kit
13-4x10-8

MBr
17-4x13-6

Dining
15-4x11-6

72'-0"

W D

Dn

Foyer

Up

Living
13-4x13-6

Porch

Garage
21-4x29-8

© Copyright by designer/architect

First Floor
1,852 sq. ft.

SPECIAL FEATURES

3,657 total square feet of living area

Dramatic two-story foyer has a stylish niche, a convenient powder room and French doors leading to the parlor

State-of-the-art kitchen includes a large walk-in pantry, breakfast island, computer center and 40' vista through family room with walk-in wet bar

Vaulted master bath features marble steps and Roman columns that lead to a majestic-sized whirlpool tub with a surrounding marble deck and grand-scale palladian window

A Jack and Jill bath, hall bath, loft area and huge bedrooms comprise the second floor

4 bedrooms, 3 1/2 baths, 3-car side entry garage

Basement foundation

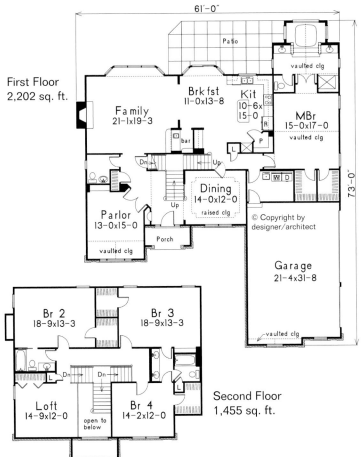

First Floor
2,202 sq. ft.

61'-0"

Patio

vaulted clg

Family
21-1x19-3

Brk fst
11-0x13-8

Kit
10-6x
15-0

MBr
15-0x17-0

vaulted clg

bar

Dn

Up

L   P
R

W D

Dining
14-0x12-0
raised clg

Up

© Copyright by
designer/architect

73'-0"

Parlor
13-0x15-0

Porch

Garage
21-4x31-8

vaulted clg

vaulted clg

Br 2
18-9x13-3

Br 3
18-9x13-3

Dn   Dn

Loft
14-9x12-0

open to
below

Br 4
14-2x12-0

Second Floor
1,455 sq. ft.

SPECIAL FEATURES

2,438 total square feet of living area

Three second floor bedrooms surround the balcony overlooking the great room

Laundry/mud room located between kitchen and garage is convenient

First floor master bedroom includes lots of closetspace and a luxury bath

2" x 6" exterior walls available, please order plan #536-058D-0091

4 bedrooms, 2 1/2 baths, 2-car garage

Basement foundation

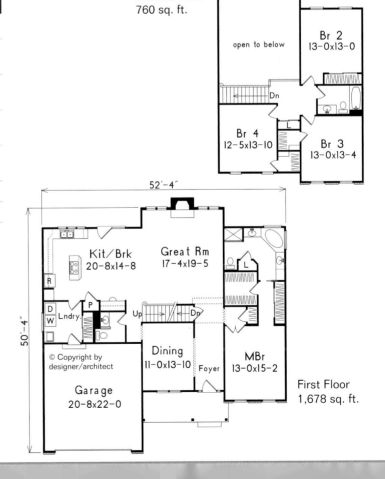

Second Floor
760 sq. ft.

open to below

Br 2
13-0x13-0

Br 4
12-5x13-10

Br 3
13-0x13-4

52'-4"

50'-4"

Kit/Brk
20-8x14-8

Great Rm
17-4x19-5

Lndry.

Up

Dn

Dining
11-0x13-10

Foyer

MBr
13-0x15-2

Garage
20-8x22-0

© Copyright by designer/architect

First Floor
1,678 sq. ft.

LEGACY SERIES

SPECIAL FEATURES

2,820 total square feet of living area

Convenient wet bar is located between the kitchen and family room

Kitchen, breakfast room and large family room flow together for informal entertaining

Luxurious master bedroom suite enjoys a fireplace and generous closet

Oversized foyer leads to private living and dining rooms

4 bedrooms, 2 1/2 baths, 2-car garage

Basement foundation, drawings also include slab and crawl space foundations

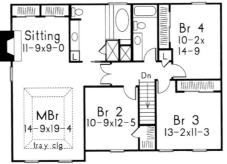

Second Floor
1,312 sq. ft.

Sitting
11-9x9-0

MBr
14-9x19-4
tray clg

Br 2
10-9x12-5

Br 4
10-2x
14-9

Dn

Br 3
13-2x11-3

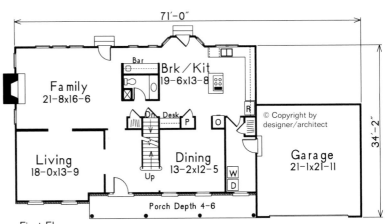

71'-0"

34'-2"

Bar

Brk/Kit
19-6x13-8

Family
21-8x16-6

Dn   Desk   P

O

R

© Copyright by
designer/architect

Living
18-0x13-9

Up

Dining
13-2x12-5

W
D

Garage
21-1x21-11

Porch Depth 4-6

First Floor
1,508 sq. ft.

SPECIAL FEATURES

2,698 total square feet of living area

An amazing grand master suite features his and hers bath spaces, an adjacent library with full wall of bookshelves and its own morning kitchen

A second floor laundry room makes this household chore a breeze

The screened porch easily provides a place for outdoor dining

4 bedrooms, 4 baths, 4-car side entry garage

Basement foundation

Second Floor
1,454 sq. ft.

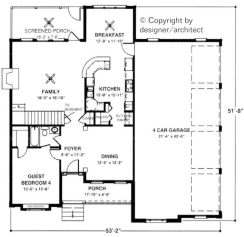

© Copyright by designer/architect

First Floor
1,244 sq. ft.

SPECIAL FEATURES

3,814 total square feet of living area

Massive sunken great room with vaulted ceiling includes exciting balcony overlook of towering atrium window wall

Seven vaulted rooms for drama and four fireplaces for warmth

Master bath is complemented by the colonnade and fireplace surrounding the sunken tub and deck

3 bedrooms, 2 1/2 baths, 3-car side entry garage

Walk-out basement foundation

3,566 square feet on the first floor and 248 square feet on the lower level atrium

Rear View

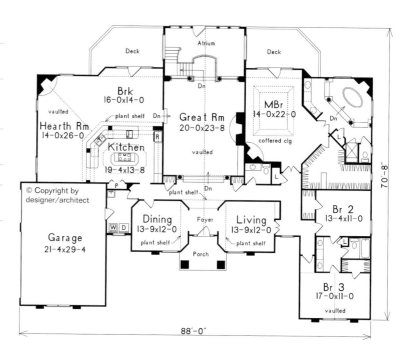

Deck — Atrium — Deck

Brk
16-0x14-0

vaulted

Hearth Rm
14-0x26-0

Kitchen
19-4x13-8

Great Rm
20-0x23-8

vaulted

MBr
14-0x22-0

coffered clg

plant shelf

plant shelf

Dn

© Copyright by designer/architect

Garage
21-4x29-4

W D

Dining
13-9x12-0

plant shelf

Foyer

Porch

Living
13-9x12-0

plant shelf

Br 2
13-4x11-0

Br 3
17-0x11-0

vaulted

70-8"

88'-0"

SPECIAL FEATURES

1,923 total square feet of living area

A spacious entrance with double coat closets invites you into the grand-sized great room with fireplace, bar area open to the kitchen with glass sliding doors to the rear patio and adjacent dining room

The large and smartly designed bay-shaped kitchen features cabinet and counter space galore with a 7' wide window above the sink for taking in the views

A luxury bath with separate shower, double entry doors, a walk-in closet and 9' wide glass sliding doors to the rear patio are many special features of the master bedroom

3 bedrooms, 2 baths, 2-car side entry garage

Slab foundation

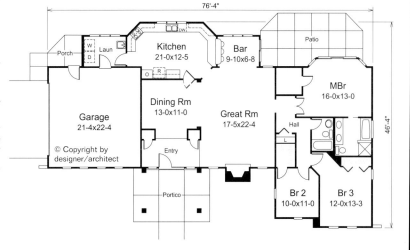

SPECIAL FEATURES

3,303 total square feet of living area

Additional family entrance from covered side porch to laundry/mud room

First floor master bedroom features two walk-in closets, luxury bath and direct access to the study

Two-story great room has a wet bar and fireplace flanked with built-ins

Open kitchen/breakfast area features a planning desk and a large pantry

2" x 6" exterior walls available, please order plan #536-058D-0093

4 bedrooms, 3 1/2 baths, 3-car side entry garage

Basement foundation

Second Floor
1,048 sq. ft.

Br 4
12-0x14-9

open to below

Br 2
17-4x14-8

Br 3
12-0x16-1

Dn

60'-8"

Deck

Kit/Brk
23-4x15-4

Great Room
18-9x21-7

63'-0"

MBr
15-4x15-8

Laundry

Porch

Up   Dn

© Copyright by designer/architect

Study
15-4x14-8

Foyer

Dining
12-0x14-8

Garage
20-4x32-8

Porch

First Floor
2,255 sq. ft.

SPECIAL FEATURES

2,470 total square feet of living area

The master suite runs the length of the house with two closets, an open bathroom and a fitness suite

Central staircase separate the family room and dining area while maintaining the flow of the rooms

The large room located on the second floor makes a great space for children to play

The future area on the second floor has an additional 371 square feet of living space

4 bedrooms, 4 baths, 3-car side entry garage

Basement foundation

Second Floor
554 sq. ft.

FUTURE AREA
11'-8" x 25'
371 Sq. Ft.

OPEN TO BELOW

BEDROOM 4
13'-4" x 11'-7"

BEDROOM 3
11' x 14'

First Floor
1,916 sq. ft.

SCREENED PORCH
18'-11" x 13'-4"

3-CAR GARAGE
21'-4" x 29'-4"

SITTING

MASTER SUITE
15' x 18'-6"
Tray Ceiling

Entertainment Center

FAMILY
19'-4" x 15'-5"

KITCHEN
11' x 13'

BREAKFAST
10'-4" x 13'

Hers   His

Tray Ceiling

Coats

Island

Desk

62'-0"

Pantry

ENTRY
8' x 11'-10"

DINING
11' x 13'

Up
Dn

Linen

FITNESS SUITE
12' x 9'-8"

PORCH
18'-8" x 6'

BEDROOM 2
11'-11" x 13'

© Copyright by designer/architect

57'-0"

LEGACY
SERIES

2603

SPECIAL FEATURES

2,271 total square feet of living area

A bay window accents the exterior while flooding the living room with cheerful light

The kitchen/breakfast area flows into the family room for a massive casual living space

A vaulted ceiling crowns the second floor master bedroom

3 bedrooms, 2 1/2 baths, 2-car garage

Basement foundation

Second Floor
973 sq. ft.

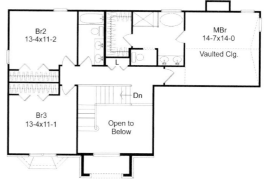

Br2
13-4x11-2

MBr
14-7x14-0

Vaulted Clg.

L

Dn

Br3
13-4x11-1

Open to
Below

First Floor
1,298 sq. ft.

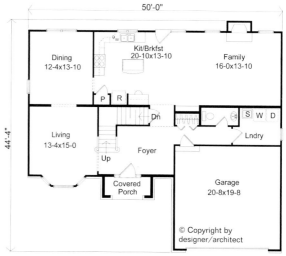

50'-0"

44'-4"

Dining
12-4x13-10

Kit/Brkfst
20-10x13-10

W

Family
16-0x13-10

P   R

Dn

S   W   D

Living
13-4x15-0

Lndry

Foyer

Up

Covered
Porch

Garage
20-8x19-8

© Copyright by
designer/architect

SPECIAL FEATURES

2,328 total square feet of living area

Formal living and dining rooms feature floor-to-ceiling windows

Kitchen with island counter and pantry makes cooking a delight

Expansive master bedroom has luxury bath with double vanity and walk-in closet

4 bedrooms, 2 1/2 baths, 2-car garage

Basement foundation, drawings also include slab and crawl space foundations

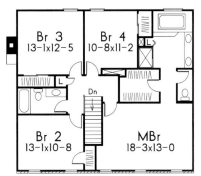

Second Floor
1,140 sq. ft.

Br 3
13-1x12-5

Br 4
10-8x11-2

Br 2
13-1x10-8

MBr
18-3x13-0

Dn

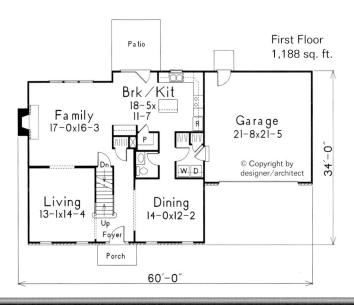

First Floor
1,188 sq. ft.

Patio

Brk/Kit
18-5x
11-7

Garage
21-8x21-5

Family
17-0x16-3

© Copyright by designer/architect

Living
13-1x14-4

Dining
14-0x12-2

Dn

Up

Foyer

Porch

34'-0"

60'-0"

SPECIAL FEATURES

3,411 total square feet of living area

Foyer opens to a large study
with raised ceiling

Master bedroom features an octagon-
shaped raised ceiling and private bath with
double vanities and corner whirlpool tub

Expansive windows and a two-way
fireplace enhance the great room

3 bedrooms, 3 baths, 3-car garage

Basement foundation

First Floor
2,182 sq. ft.

© Copyright by
designer/architect

Lower Level
1,229 sq. ft.

SPECIAL FEATURES

2,360 total square feet of living area

Ample-sized living and dining rooms directly off the foyer

Family room is enhanced with built-in bookshelves and a cozy fireplace

Master bedroom is complemented with a spacious walk-in closet and private bath with skylight

4 bedrooms, 2 1/2 baths, 2-car garage

Partial basement/crawl space foundation, drawings also include crawl space and slab foundations

Second Floor
727 sq. ft.

Bed 1
13-4x13-6

Bed 2
12-7x10-4

Bed 3
12-8x10-3

Attic

First Floor
1,633 sq. ft.

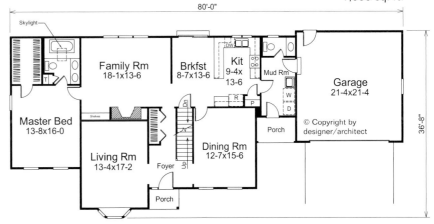

80'-0"

36'-8"

Skylight

Family Rm
18-1x13-6

Brkfst
8-7x13-6

Kit
9-4x
13-6

Mud Rm

Garage
21-4x21-4

Master Bed
13-8x16-0

Shelves

Living Rm
13-4x17-2

Foyer

Dining Rm
12-7x15-6

Porch

© Copyright by designer/architect

Porch

Porch

SPECIAL FEATURES

3,494 total square feet of living area

Majestic two-story foyer opens into
the living and dining rooms, both
framed by arched columns

Balcony overlooks the large living area
featuring French doors to a covered porch

Luxurious master bedroom

Convenient game room
supports lots of activities

4 bedrooms, 3 1/2 baths,
3-car side entry garage

Slab foundation, drawings also
include crawl space foundation

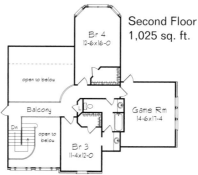

Second Floor
1,025 sq. ft.

Br 4
12-6x16-0

open to below

Balcony

Dn

open to below

Br 3
11-4x12-0

Game Rm
14-6x17-4

First Floor
2,469 sq. ft.

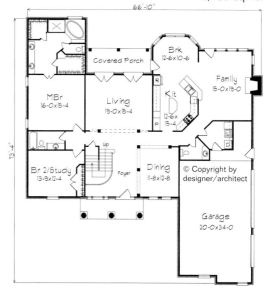

66'-10"

Brk
12-6x10-6

Covered Porch

Family
15-0x19-0

MBr
16-0x15-4

Living
19-0x15-4

Kit
12-6x
15-4

73'-4"

Br 2/Study
13-9x12-4

up

Foyer

Dining
11-8x12-8

© Copyright by
designer/architect

Garage
20-0x34-0

LOWE'S
LEGACY
SERIES

SPECIAL FEATURES

2,240 total square feet of living area

Floor plan makes good use of space above garage allowing for four bedrooms and a bonus room on the second floor

Formal dining room is easily accessible to the kitchen

Cozy family room features a fireplace and sunny bay window

Bonus room on the second floor is included in the square footage

2" x 6" exterior walls available, please order plan #536-058D-0089

4 bedrooms, 2 1/2 baths, 2-car garage

Basement foundation

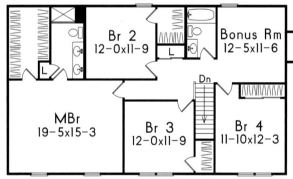

Second Floor
1,344 sq. ft.

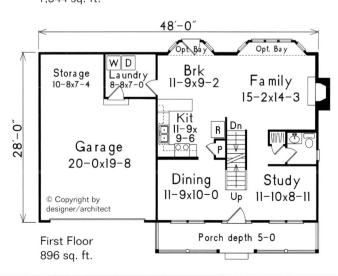

First Floor
896 sq. ft.

SPECIAL FEATURES

2,387 total square feet of living area

Wide open kitchen, breakfast and family rooms look out to the rear courtyard

Second floor features three large bedrooms all with walk-in closets

Master bedroom has two walk-in closets and a luxurious bath

3 bedrooms, 2 1/2 baths, 2-car side entry garage

Basement foundation

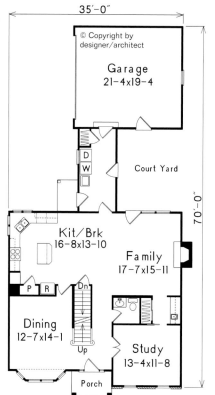

35'-0"

© Copyright by designer/architect

Garage
21-4x19-4

Court Yard

First Floor
1,278 sq. ft.

70'-0"

Kit/Brk
16-8x13-10

Family
17-7x15-11

D
W

P   R

Dn

Dining
12-7x14-1

Up

Study
13-4x11-8

Porch

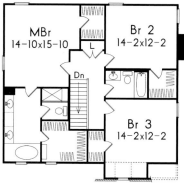

Second Floor
1,109 sq. ft.

MBr
14-10x15-10

Br 2
14-2x12-2

L

Dn

Br 3
14-2x12-2

2003

SPECIAL FEATURES

2,304 total square feet of living area

Stately foyer with ascending staircase and access to the living and dining rooms

Well-organized kitchen includes a pass-through peninsula and spacious pantry

Powder room is adjacent to first floor laundry

Roomy master bedroom enjoys double closets

4 bedrooms, 2 1/2 baths, 2-car garage

Basement foundation, drawings also include crawl space and slab foundations

Second Floor
1,152 sq. ft.

Bed 2
14-1x12-0

Bed 3
10-4x12-0

Bed 4
14-1x14-3

Master Bed
14-2x16-7

First Floor
1,152 sq. ft.

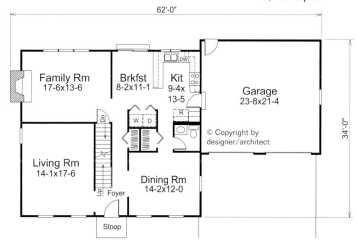

62'-0"

Family Rm
17-6x13-6

Brkfst
8-2x11-1

Kit
9-4x
13-5

Garage
23-8x21-4

© Copyright by designer/architect

34'-0"

Living Rm
14-1x17-6

Dining Rm
14-2x12-0

Foyer

Stoop

SPECIAL FEATURES

3,013 total square feet of living area

Varying roof lines create an
exciting exterior look

Unique interior has countless
innovative features

Large activity room and hall to laundry
area feature a curving window wall
that surrounds the outdoor atrium

Kitchen opens to a sun-drenched nook
with sloped ceiling and skylights

Master bedroom boasts a luxurious
step-up vaulted bath with Roman
tub, separate shower/toilet area
and an enormous walk-in closet

3 bedrooms, 3 baths, 2-car garage

Partial basement/crawl space foundation

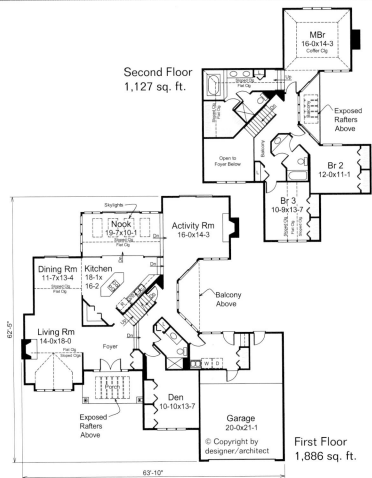

Second Floor
1,127 sq. ft.

MBr
16-0x14-3
Coffer Clg

Sloped Clg
Flat Clg

Up

Exposed
Rafters
Above

Sloped Clg
Flat Clg

Open to
Foyer Below

Balcony

Br 2
12-0x11-1

Br 3
10-9x13-7

Skylights

Nook
19-7x10-1
Sloped Clg
Flat Clg

Activity Rm
16-0x14-3

Dining Rm
11-7x13-4
Sloped Clg
Flat Clg

Kitchen
18-1x
16-2

Balcony
Above

Living Rm
14-0x18-0
Flat Clg
Sloped Clg

Foyer

Porch

Den
10-10x13-7

Garage
20-0x21-1

Exposed
Rafters
Above

W   D

© Copyright by
designer/architect

First Floor
1,886 sq. ft.

62'-5"

63'-10"

LOWE'S LEGACY SERIES

SPECIAL FEATURES

3,160 total square feet of living area

Covered entry porch leads into a magnificent two-story foyer that accesses formal rooms on either side

First floor master bedroom features two walk-in closets and a large master bath

Kitchen is designed for efficiency and includes island cooktop and pass-through to the breakfast room

4 bedrooms, 3 1/2 baths, 3-car side entry garage

Basement foundation

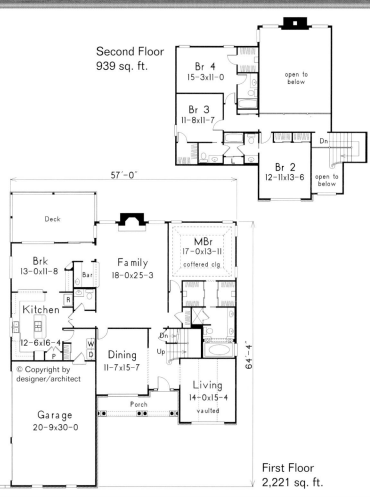

Second Floor
939 sq. ft.

Br 4
15-3x11-0

open to below

Br 3
11-8x11-7

Br 2
12-11x13-6

open to below

Dn

57'-0"

Deck

Brk
13-0x11-8

Bar

Kitchen

12-6x16-4

P

W
D

R

Family
18-0x25-3

Dining
11-7x15-7

Dn

Up

MBr
17-0x13-11

coffered clg

Living
14-0x15-4

vaulted

Porch

© Copyright by designer/architect

Garage
20-9x30-0

64'-4"

First Floor
2,221 sq. ft.

SPECIAL FEATURES

3,073 total square feet of living area

Fireplace creates a cozy feeling in the family room

All bedrooms are located on the second floor for privacy

Kitchen is placed between the breakfast nook and formal dining room for maximum convenience

Two-story foyer adds spaciousness and light

4 bedrooms, 2 1/2 baths, 2-car side entry garage

Basement foundation

Second Floor
1,828 sq. ft.

Br 2
12-5x12-8

Br 3
13-0x13-0

Br 1
12-6x15-3

Open to Foyer Below

MBr
22-0x24-11

Sloped Clg

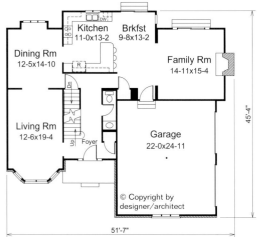

First Floor
1,245 sq. ft.

Kitchen
11-0x13-2

Brkfst
9-8x13-2

Dining Rm
12-5x14-10

Family Rm
14-11x15-4

Living Rm
12-6x19-4

Foyer

Garage
22-0x24-11

45'-4"

51'-7"

© Copyright by designer/architect

LOWE'S
LEGACY
SERIES

SPECIAL FEATURES

1,725 total square feet of living area

Loft offers private niche
overlooking foyer and living room

Kitchen and breakfast rooms are
separated by the breakfast bar

Master bedroom features double walk-in
closets, large vanity and private bath area

2" x 6" exterior walls available,
please order plan #536-001D-0115

3 bedrooms, 2 baths, 2-car garage

Crawl space foundation, drawings also
include basement and slab foundations

Second Floor
645 sq. ft.

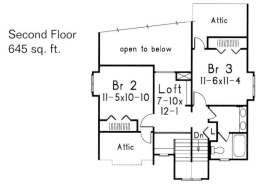

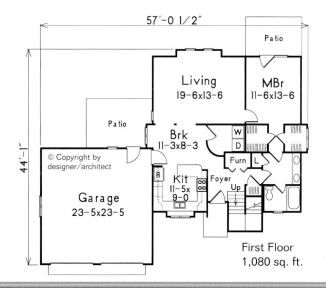

First Floor
1,080 sq. ft.

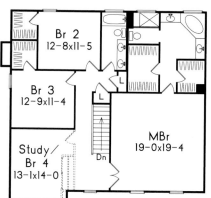

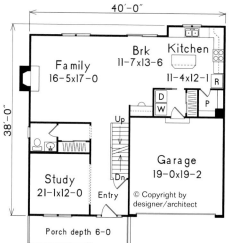

LEGACY SERIES

SPECIAL FEATURES

2,547 total square feet of living area

Energy efficient home with
2" x 6" exterior walls

Second floor makes economical use of
area above garage allowing for three
bedrooms and a study/fourth bedroom

First floor study is ideal for a home office

Large pantry is located in
the efficient kitchen

3 bedrooms, 2 1/2 baths, 2-car garage

Basement foundation

Second Floor
1,464 sq. ft.

Br 2
12-8x11-5

Br 3
12-9x11-4

Study/
Br 4
13-1x14-0

MBr
19-0x19-4

Dn

First Floor
1,083 sq. ft.

40'-0"

38'-0"

Family
16-5x17-0

Brk
11-7x13-6

Kitchen
11-4x12-1

D
W
P
R

Up

Study
21-1x12-0

Dn

Garage
19-0x19-2

Entry

© Copyright by
designer/architect

Porch depth 6-0

SPECIAL FEATURES

3,376 total square feet of living area

The entry draws guests in with the circular stair and 18' vaulted ceiling

Triple 8' high French doors provide a view of the backyard from the family room

Bedrooms #3 and #4 share a Jack and Jill bath

4 bedrooms, 3 1/2 baths, 2-car side entry garage

Walk-out basement foundation

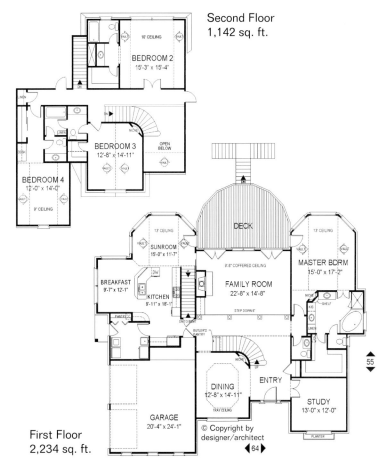

Second Floor
1,142 sq. ft.

First Floor
2,234 sq. ft.

© Copyright by designer/architect

SPECIAL FEATURES

5,321 total square feet of living area

The combination of stone, brick, multiple gables and roof dormers creates an exciting and sophisticated structure

A two-story entry foyer and wide, finely crafted staircase with niche is inviting and elegant

The kitchen includes a bayed breakfast room, hearth room with fireplace and is convenient to a large dining room with butler's pantry

The master bedroom with sitting room and sumptuous bath is unsurpassed in luxury

4 bedrooms, 5 1/2 baths, 3-car rear entry garage

Basement foundation

Second Floor
1,784 sq. ft.

First Floor
3,537 sq. ft.

© Copyright by designer/architect

Lowe's LEGACY SERIES

SPECIAL FEATURES

3,850 total square feet of living area

Entry, with balcony above, leads into a splendid great room with sunken solarium

Kitchen layout boasts a half-circle bar and cooktop island with banquet-sized dining nearby

Solarium features U-shaped staircase with balcony and an arched window

Master bedroom includes a luxurious bath and large study with bay window

5 bedrooms, 3 1/2 baths, 3-car garage

Basement foundation

Interior View - Sunken Solarium

Second Floor
1,544 sq. ft.

Br 5 12-1x14-3 · Sunken Solarium Below · Br 2 13-11x15-9 · Loft · Dn · Br 4 12-1x12-0 · Library 15-8x9-8 · Br 3 15-5x12-0 · open to below

First Floor
2,306 sq. ft.

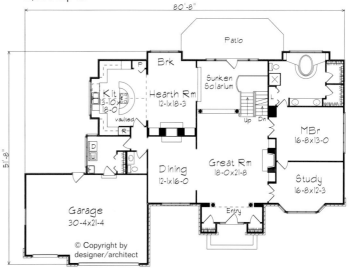

80'-8"

Patio · Brk · Kit 13-0x18-0 vaulted · Hearth Rm 12-1x18-3 · Sunken Solarium · Up · Dn · MBr 16-8x13-0 · Dining 12-1x16-0 · Great Rm 18-0x21-8 · Study 16-8x12-3 · Garage 30-4x21-4 · Entry

© Copyright by designer/architect

SPECIAL FEATURES

3,503 total square feet of living area

Entry foyer leads to
an elegant curved stairway

Family room features a 14' ceiling and
a fireplace flanked by windows

Study, tucked away from the traffic area,
features one full wall of built-in bookcases

5 bedrooms, 3 1/2 baths

Slab foundation

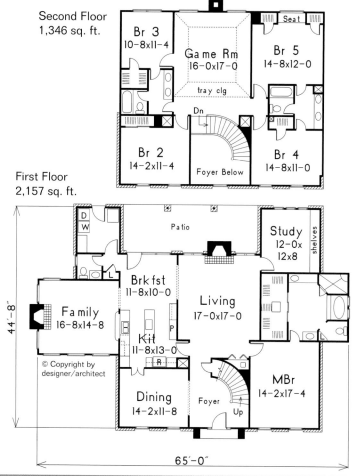

Second Floor
1,346 sq. ft.

Br 3
10-8x11-4

Game Rm
16-0x17-0
tray clg

Seat

Br 5
14-8x12-0

Dn

Br 2
14-2x11-4

Foyer Below

Br 4
14-8x11-0

First Floor
2,157 sq. ft.

D
W

Patio

Study
12-0x
12x8

shelves

Brk fst
11-8x10-0

Living
17-0x17-0

L

Family
16-8x14-8

Kit
11-8x13-0

P

© Copyright by
designer/architect

R

44'-8"

Dining
14-2x11-8

Foyer

Up

MBr
14-2x17-4

65'-0"

SPECIAL FEATURES

2,510 total square feet of living area

Energy efficient home with
2" x 6" exterior walls

Both formal and informal living spaces
are graced with stylish fireplaces

Enjoy the large deck and sunroom
located off the dining room

All of the bedrooms are located on the
second floor, including the master suite
complete with a private balcony

3 bedrooms, 2 1/2 baths, 2-car garage

Basement foundation

Second Floor
1,086 sq. ft.

Balcony

Br 1
12-0x15-7

Br 2
11-9x12-4

MBr
13-0x15-8

DN.

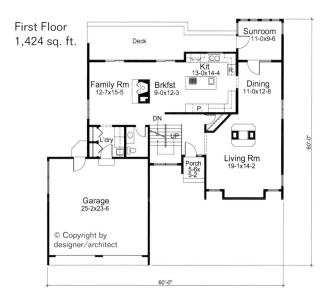

First Floor
1,424 sq. ft.

Deck

Sunroom
11-0x9-6

Kit
13-0x14-4

Family Rm
12-7x15-5

Brkfst
9-0x12-3

Dining
11-0x12-8

DN

P.

L'dry

UP

Living Rm
19-1x14-2

Porch
5-6x
5-2

Garage
25-2x23-6

© Copyright by
designer/architect

60'-0"

60'-0"

SPECIAL FEATURES

2,174 total square feet of living area

The first floor features 9' ceilings

The bayed breakfast area includes a built-in desk, pantry and access to the outdoors

The master bedroom enjoys an abundance of storage space with two large walk-in closets

The laundry area is conveniently located near the bedrooms

3 bedrooms, 2 1/2 baths, 2-car side entry garage

Basement foundation

Second Floor
1,091 sq. ft.

MBr
13-8x17-1

Br 2
11-1x12-1

Br 3
11-3x12-4

First Floor
1,083 sq. ft.

52'-0"

46'-0"

Family
13-8x15-8

Brkfst
13-0x11-11

Kit.
12-4x11-11

Porch
14-0x5-8

Dining
13-8x12-4

Mud Rm

Garage
21-0x23-4

© Copyright by designer/architect

Lowe's LEGACY SERIES

SPECIAL FEATURES

2,678 total square feet of living area

Open foyer is graced
with an elegant circular stair

Colossal-sized living room
leads to a covered rear porch

Spacious bedrooms provide
generous closet space

Second floor balcony views foyer below

4 bedrooms, 2 1/2 baths,
2-car side entry garage

Basement foundation

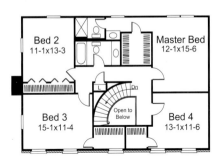

Second Floor
1,164 sq. ft.

Bed 2
11-1x13-3

Master Bed
12-1x15-6

Bed 3
15-1x11-4

Open to
Below

Bed 4
13-1x11-6

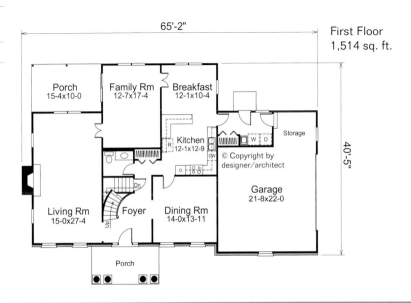

First Floor
1,514 sq. ft.

65'-2"

40'-5"

Porch
15-4x10-0

Family Rm
12-7x17-4

Breakfast
12-1x10-4

Kitchen
12-1x12-9

Storage

© Copyright by
designer/architect

Garage
21-8x22-0

Living Rm
15-0x27-4

Foyer

Dining Rm
14-0x13-11

Porch

SPECIAL FEATURES

2,733 total square feet of living area

Energy efficient home
with 2" x 6" exterior walls

9' ceilings throughout the first floor

Master bedroom features a
double-door entry, large bay window
and master bath with walk-in closet
and separate tub and shower

Efficiently designed kitchen adjoins
an octagon-shaped breakfast nook,
which opens to the outdoors

4 bedrooms, 2 1/2 baths, 2-car garage

Basement foundation

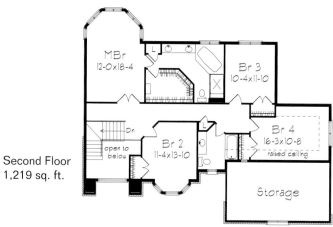

Second Floor
1,219 sq. ft.

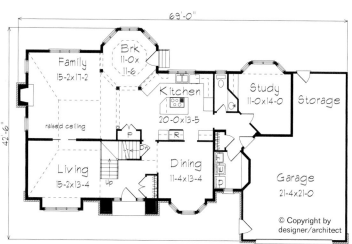

First Floor
1,514 sq. ft.

© Copyright by
designer/architect

SPECIAL FEATURES

2,805 total square feet of living area

Wrap-around counter in the kitchen opens to a bayed breakfast area

Great room features a grand fireplace flanked by doors that access the rear covered porch

Secondary bedrooms enjoy walk-in closets

The extra-large utility room offers an abundance of workspace

4 bedrooms, 3 baths, 2-car side entry garage

Basement foundation, drawings also include crawl space and slab foundations

© Copyright by designer/architect

WIDTH: 71' - 0"
DEPTH: 70' - 0"

LOWE'S LEGACY SERIES

SPECIAL FEATURES

2,695 total square feet of living area

A grand-scale great room features a fireplace with flanking shelves, handsome entry foyer with staircase and opens to a large kitchen and breakfast room

Roomy master bedroom has a bay window, huge walk-in closet and bath

Bedrooms #2 and #3 are generously oversized with walk-in closets and a Jack and Jill style bath

2" x 6" exterior walls available, please order plan #536-007E-0117

3 bedrooms, 2 1/2 baths, 2-car side entry garage

Basement foundation

76'-0"

55'-2"

Patio

MBr
18-8x17-0

Brk Rm
14-10x11-1

MBath

Br 2
14-0x14-1

Great Room
18-6x23-0

Kit
15-2x11-4

L

P   R

Dn

Br 3
14-0x14-8

Entry

Dining
13-2x15-0

W
D

Garage
21-4x20-10

Porch

tray clg.

© Copyright by designer/architect

SPECIAL FEATURES

2,716 total square feet of living area

9' ceilings throughout the first floor

All bedrooms boast walk-in closets

Great room and hearth room share a see-through fireplace

Balcony overlooks the large great room

4 bedrooms, 4 1/2 baths, 2-car side entry garage

Basement foundation

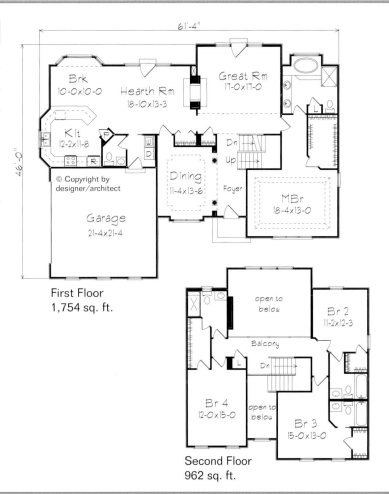

First Floor
1,754 sq. ft.

Second Floor
962 sq. ft.

SPECIAL FEATURES

2,964 total square feet of living area

Two amazing two-story screened porches is perfect for enjoying the outdoors without having to endure the elements

Beautiful brick facade creates an attractive and elegant exterior that offers great curb appeal

Brilliant floor plan flows beautifully and creates many large areas perfect for gathering space

4 bedrooms, 4 baths, 3-car side entry garage

Basement foundation

Rear View

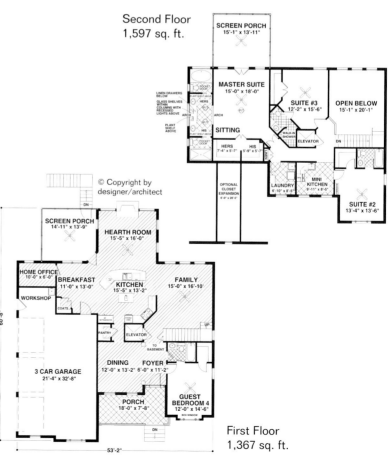

Second Floor
1,597 sq. ft.

SCREEN PORCH
15'-1" x 13'-11"

MASTER SUITE
15'-0" x 18'-0"

SUITE #3
12'-2" x 15'-6"

OPEN BELOW
15'-1" x 20'-1"

LINEN DRAWERS BELOW

GLASS SHELVES WITHIN COLUMNS WITH RECESSED LIGHTS ABOVE

HERS

ARCH

PLANT SHELF ABOVE

SITTING

WALK-IN SHOWER

ELEVATOR

DN

HERS
7'-4" x 5'-7"

HIS
5'-9" x 5'-7"

OPTIONAL CLOSET EXPANSION
6'-0" x 20'-5"

LAUNDRY
6'-10" x 8'-5"

MINI KITCHEN
9'-11" x 8'-5"

SUITE #2
13'-4" x 13'-6"

© Copyright by designer/architect

SCREEN PORCH
14'-11" x 13'-9"

HEARTH ROOM
15'-5" x 16'-0"

HOME OFFICE
10'-0" x 6'-0"

BREAKFAST
11'-0" x 13'-0"

KITCHEN
15'-5" x 13'-2"

FAMILY
15'-0" x 16'-10"

WORKSHOP

COATS.

PANTRY

ELEVATOR

UP

TO BASEMENT

3 CAR GARAGE
21'-4" x 32'-8"

DINING
12'-0" x 13'-2"

FOYER
6'-0" x 11'-2"

GUEST BEDROOM 4
12'-0" x 14'-6"

PORCH
18'-0" x 7'-8"

BOX WINDOW

DN

60'-8"

53'-2"

First Floor
1,367 sq. ft.

SPECIAL FEATURES

3,412 total square feet of living area

Large formal dining room with vaulted ceiling is adjacent to the entry foyer

Expansive great room boasts a dramatic fireplace and vaulted ceiling

Master bedroom and library are secluded from other living areas

Family-style kitchen/breakfast area includes pantry, island cooktop and large breakfast area

Sunken master bedroom has patio access and a luxurious private bath

3 bedrooms, 3 baths, 2-car side entry garage

Basement foundation

SPECIAL FEATURES

2,954 total square feet of living area

Master bedroom has a double-door entry into the luxurious bath

Private study has direct access into the master bedroom

Vaulted ceiling and bay window add light and dimension to the breakfast room

4 bedrooms, 3 1/2 baths, 2-car side entry garage

Basement foundation, drawings also include crawl space foundation

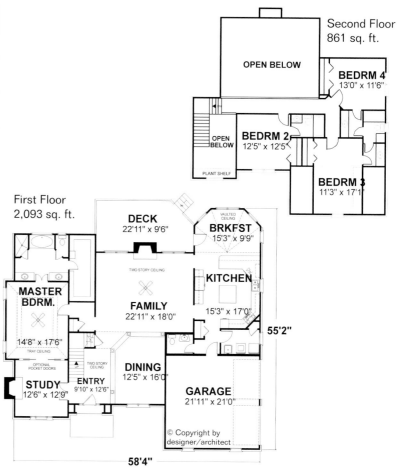

Second Floor
861 sq. ft.

OPEN BELOW

BEDRM 4
13'0" x 11'6"

OPEN BELOW

BEDRM 2
12'5" x 12'5"

PLANT SHELF

BEDRM 3
11'3" x 17'1"

First Floor
2,093 sq. ft.

DECK
22'11" x 9'6"

BRKFST
15'3" x 9'9"
VAULTED CEILING

TWO STORY CEILING

KITCHEN
15'3" x 17'0"

MASTER BDRM.
14'8" x 17'6"
TRAY CEILING

FAMILY
22'11" x 18'0"

55'2"

OPTIONAL POCKET DOORS

TWO STORY CEILING

DINING
12'5" x 16'0"

STUDY
12'6" x 12'9"

ENTRY
9'10" x 12'6"

GARAGE
21'11" x 21'0"

© Copyright by designer/architect

58'4"

SPECIAL FEATURES

3,267 total square feet of living area

Gourmet kitchen features a walk-in pantry

Double walk-in closets in
the master bedroom

Luxury master bath features a linen
closet and a separate tub and shower

Three bedrooms, two baths and a
charming loft area complete the
second floor of this family home

4 bedrooms, 3 1/2 baths,
3-car side entry garage

Basement foundation

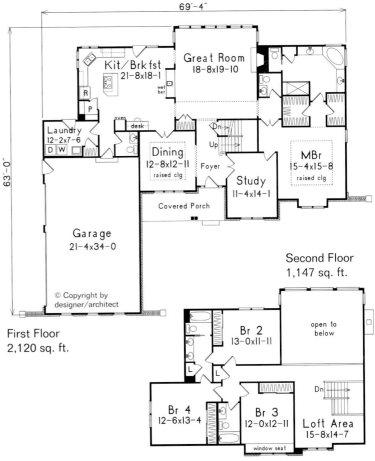

69'-4"

63'-0"

Kit/Brkfst
21-8x18-1

Great Room
18-8x19-10

wet bar

R

P

oven

desk

Laundry
12-2x7-6

D W

Dining
12-8x12-11
raised clg

Dn

Up

Foyer

MBr
15-4x15-8
raised clg

Study
11-4x14-1

Covered Porch

Garage
21-4x34-0

© Copyright by
designer/architect

First Floor
2,120 sq. ft.

Second Floor
1,147 sq. ft.

Br 2
13-0x11-11

open to
below

Br 4
12-6x13-4

Br 3
12-0x12-11

Dn

Loft Area
15-8x14-7

window seat

L

L

SPECIAL FEATURES

2,520 total square feet of living area

Open hearth fireplace warms the
family and breakfast rooms

Master bedroom features a private
bath with deluxe tub, double-bowl
vanity and large walk-in closet

Vaulted living and dining
rooms flank the foyer

Corner sink in kitchen overlooks
the family and breakfast rooms

4 bedrooms, 2 1/2 baths,
2-car side entry garage

Basement foundation, drawings also
include crawl space and slab foundations

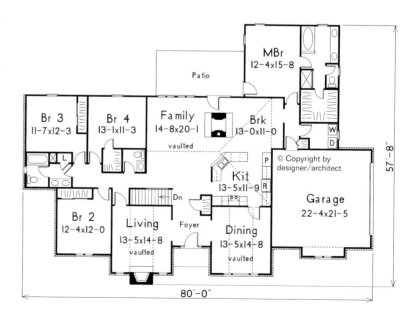

Patio

MBr
12-4x15-8

Br 3
11-7x12-3

Br 4
13-1x11-3

Family
14-8x20-1
vaulted

Brk
13-0x11-0

Kit
13-5x11-9

© Copyright by
designer/architect

Garage
22-4x21-5

Br 2
12-4x12-0

Living
13-5x14-8
vaulted

Dn

Foyer

Dining
13-5x14-8
vaulted

57'-8"

80'-0"

SPECIAL FEATURES

2,511 total square feet of living area

Energy efficient home with
2" x 6" exterior walls

Kitchen, breakfast and living
rooms feature tray ceilings

Architectural elements combine to
create an impressive exterior

Master bedroom includes large
walk-in closet, oversized bay window
and private bath with shower and tub

4 bedrooms, 2 1/2 baths,
3-car side entry garage

Basement foundation, drawings also
include crawl space and slab foundations

Second Floor
1,174 sq. ft.

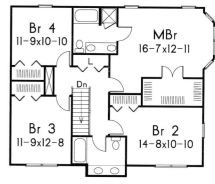

Br 4
11-9x10-10

MBr
16-7x12-11

Dn

Br 3
11-9x12-8

Br 2
14-8x10-10

First Floor
1,337 sq. ft.

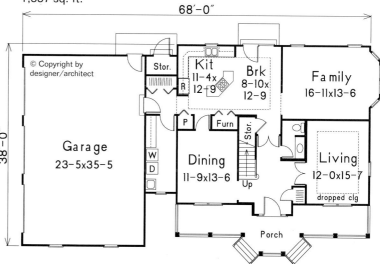

68'-0"

38'-0"

© Copyright by
designer/architect

Stor.

Kit
11-4x
12-9

Brk
8-10x
12-9

Family
16-11x13-6

Garage
23-5x35-5

Furn
Stor.
P

W
D

Dining
11-9x13-6

Up

Living
12-0x15-7

dropped clg

Porch

SPECIAL FEATURES

2,801 total square feet of living area

9' ceilings on the first floor

Full view dining bay with elegant circle-top windows

Wrap-around porches provide outdoor exposure in all directions

Secluded master bedroom with double vanities and walk-in closets

Convenient game room

5 bedrooms, 3 baths, 2-car side entry garage

Slab foundation

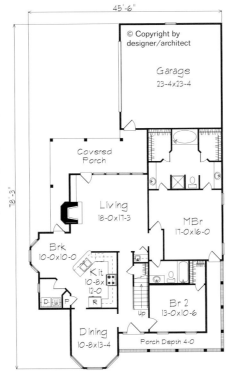

45'-6"

78'-3"

© Copyright by designer/architect

Garage
23-4x23-4

Covered Porch

Living
18-0x17-3

MBr
17-0x16-0

Brk
10-0x10-0

Kit
10-8x12-0

Br 2
13-0x10-6

Dining
10-8x13-4

Porch Depth 4-0

Up

D W P R

First Floor
1,651 sq. ft.

Br 3
13-3x13-3

Game Rm
17-0x10-10

Br 4
14-4x13-0

Br 5
17-2x12-0

Dn

Second Floor
1,150 sq. ft.

SPECIAL FEATURES

2,307 total square feet of living area

The bayed breakfast area warms
the home with natural light

The spacious master bedroom boasts
two walk-in closets, a private bath and a
bonus area ideal for an office or nursery

The vaulted great room includes a
grand fireplace, built-in shelves and a
double-door entry onto the covered porch

3 bedrooms, 2 1/2 baths,
2-car side entry garage

Basement foundation, drawings also
include crawl space and slab foundations

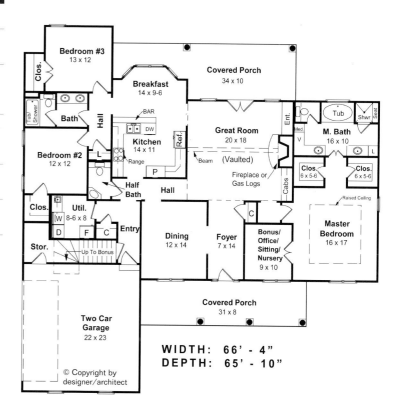

WIDTH: 66' - 4"
DEPTH: 65' - 10"

SPECIAL FEATURES

2,952 total square feet of living area

An extra-large island and a walk-in pantry enhance the kitchen that opens into the cheerful breakfast area

The master bedroom enjoys the privacy of the first floor and features two walk-in closets and a deluxe bath with double-bowl vanity and whirlpool tub

Three additional bedrooms are located on the second floor and include spectacular walk-in closets and private baths

4 bedrooms, 4 full baths, 2 half baths, 3-car garage

Basement foundation

Second Floor
875 sq. ft.

Br2
12-0x13-0

Open to Below

Br3
12-0x12-0

Dn

Br4
11-4x13-0

66'-8"

61'-0"

Great Room
17-11x21-3

Brkfst
18-8x10-9

MBr
13-4x15-7
Coffered
Clg

Kitchen
18-8x12-6

Up

Dining
11-4x12-10

Lndry

Study
13-4x13-10

Covered Porch

Garage
34-0x21-4

First Floor
2,077 sq. ft.

SPECIAL FEATURES

2,859 total square feet of living area

The vaulted great room with fireplace includes sliding glass doors that lead to covered and uncovered patio areas and the stairwell that accesses the unfinished lower level

A walk-in pantry, menu/computer desk and snack island are a few highlights of the kitchen

The vaulted master bedroom includes a posh bath with separate toilet and shower areas, a "bath-in-a-solarium" with plant shelves and skylights above and sliding glass doors to a rear patio

3 bedrooms, 2 1/2 baths, 3-car side entry garage

Basement foundation

Rear View

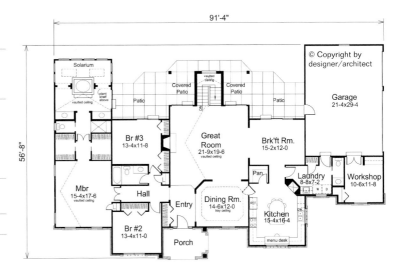

91'-4"

56'-8"

Solarium

plant shelf above

vaulted ceiling

Patio

Covered Patio

vaulted ceiling

Covered Patio

Patio

© Copyright by designer/architect

Garage
21-4x29-4

Br #3
13-4x11-8

Great Room
21-9x19-6
vaulted ceiling

Brk'ft Rm.
15-2x12-0

Pan.

Mbr
15-4x17-6
vaulted ceiling

Hall

Entry

Dining Rm.
14-6x12-0
tray ceiling

Laundry
8-8x7-2

Workshop
10-6x11-8

Br #2
13-4x11-0

Porch

Kitchen
15-4x16-4

menu desk

SPECIAL FEATURES

3,073 total square feet of living area

Living room includes a bay window
and opens to the dining room
featuring a box-bay window seat

Convenient kitchen overlooks breakfast nook
which leads into the large activity area with
fireplace and sliding doors to the rear yard

Huge master bedroom has a vaulted ceiling,
large sitting area and a lavish bath

All bedrooms have large closets
and share a hall bath

4 bedrooms, 2 1/2 baths,
2-car side entry garage

Basement foundation

Br 2
12-5x12-8

Br 3
13-0x13-0

Br 1
12-6x15-3

Open to
Foyer Below

MBr
22-0x24-11

Sloped Clg.

Second Floor
1,828 sq. ft.

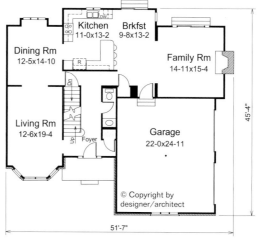

Kitchen
11-0x13-2

Brkfst
9-8x13-2

Dining Rm
12-5x14-10

Family Rm
14-11x15-4

Living Rm
12-6x19-4

Foyer

Garage
22-0x24-11

45'-4"

51'-7"

First Floor
1,245 sq. ft.

SPECIAL FEATURES

3,366 total square feet of living area

Wonderful covered patio is located off the secluded study and breakfast area

Separate dining area for entertaining

Spacious master bedroom has an enormous private bath with walk-in closet

4 bedrooms, 3 1/2 baths, 2-car side entry garage

Crawl space foundation, drawings also include slab foundation

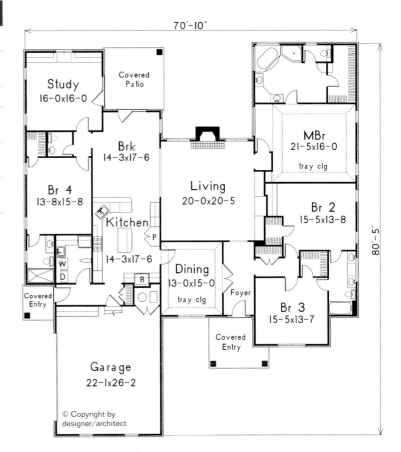

70'-10"

80'-5"

Study
16-0x16-0

Covered Patio

Brk
14-3x17-6

MBr
21-5x16-0
tray clg

Br 4
13-8x15-8

Living
20-0x20-5

Br 2
15-5x13-8

Kitchen
14-3x17-6

W
D

P

Dining
13-0x15-0
tray clg

Foyer

Br 3
15-5x13-7

R

Covered Entry

Covered Entry

Garage
22-1x26-2

© Copyright by designer/architect

SPECIAL FEATURES

2,953 total square feet of living area

The chef of the family will be delighted with this gourmet kitchen adjoined by a cozy breakfast room with a computer desk

A hidden room, cleverly concealed behind cabinet doors is located off the breakfast room providing space for a safe room, storage of valuables or security

A convenient elevator connects the first and second floors eliminating the vertical challenge of the second floor bedrooms

4 bedrooms, 4 baths, 3-car side entry garage

Basement foundation

Rear View

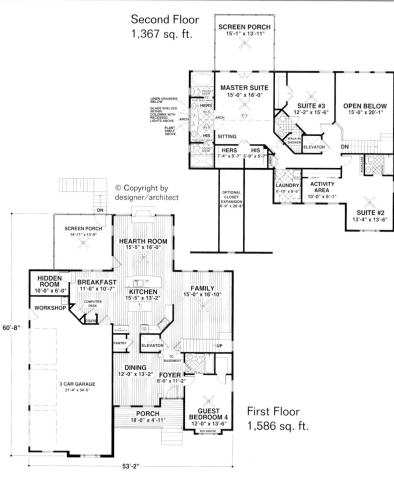

Second Floor
1,367 sq. ft.

SCREEN PORCH
15'-1" x 13'-11"

MASTER SUITE
15'-0" x 18'-0"

SUITE #3
12'-2" x 15'-6"

OPEN BELOW
15'-0" x 20'-1"

LINEN DRAWERS BELOW

GLASS SHELVES WITHIN COLUMNS WITH RECESSED LIGHTS ABOVE

HERS

PLANT SHELF ABOVE

ARCH

SITTING

HIS

PLANT SHELF ABOVE

WALK-IN SHOWER

ELEVATOR

DN

HERS
7'-4" x 5'-7"

HIS
5'-9" x 5'-7"

LINEN

BOOKCASE

LAUNDRY
6'-10" x 8'-5"

ACTIVITY AREA
10'-0" x 6'-1"

OPTIONAL CLOSET EXPANSION
6'-0" x 20'-8"

SUITE #2
13'-4" x 13'-6"

© Copyright by designer/architect

DN

SCREEN PORCH
14'-11" x 13'-9"

HEARTH ROOM
15'-5" x 16'-0"

HIDDEN ROOM
10'-0" x 6'-0"

BREAKFAST
11'-0" x 10'-7"

KITCHEN
15'-5" x 13'-2"

FAMILY
15'-0" x 16'-10"

WORKSHOP

COMPUTER DESK

COATS

REFRIGERATOR

PANTRY

ELEVATOR

TO BASEMENT

UP

3 CAR GARAGE
21'-4" x 34'-5"

DINING
12'-0" x 13'-2"

FOYER
6'-0" x 11'-2"

60'-8"

PORCH
18'-0" x 4'-11"

GUEST BEDROOM 4
12'-0" x 13'-6"

BOX WINDOW

First Floor
1,586 sq. ft.

53'-2"

Second Floor
2,202 sq. ft.

MBr
18-2x16-4
vaulted

Plant shelf above

Seat

Br 2
13-2x12-5

Br 3
13-8x13-0

Balcony

Dn

Dn

Br 4
14-0x12-1

Foyer Below

Playroom
13-8x18-8

Porch Below

SPECIAL FEATURES

4,597 total square feet of living area

A two-story palladian entrance welcomes you to a spacious foyer with second floor balcony overlook

The enormous great room with fireplace is convenient to the nearby study with window seat

A state-of-the-art kitchen offers corner windows at the sink, an island snack bar, large walk-in pantry and adjoins the laundry area with a second pantry

The master bedroom has a stylish bath and over 200 square feet of walk-in closet space

4 bedrooms, 4 1/2 baths,
3-car side entry garage

Basement foundation

First Floor
2,395 sq. ft.

66'-0"

Patio

58'-0"

Kitchen
15-0x13-8

Brk'ft Rm
15-6x19-3

Great Rm
20-0x21-7

Seat

Study
13-8x14-8

P

R

S W D P

Laundry

Desk

Up

Dn

© Copyright by
designer/architect

Dining
14-0x16-6

Up

Foyer

Living Rm
13-8x16-6

Garage
21-4x29-4

Porch

LEGACY SERIES

SPECIAL FEATURES

2,218 total square feet of living area

Energy efficient home with
2" x 6" exterior walls

The U-shaped kitchen provides plenty
of counterspace for ease while cooking
and also has a nice-sized built-in desk

The radiant breakfast room is
octagon-shaped flooding the area in sunlight

A large bath and walk-in closet
make the master bedroom
functional and stylish all in one

4 bedrooms, 3 1/2 baths,
2-car side entry garage

Basement foundation

Second Floor
867 sq. ft.

First Floor
1,351 sq. ft.

SPECIAL FEATURES

2,521 total square feet of living area

Large living and dining rooms are a plus for formal entertaining or large family gatherings

Informal kitchen, breakfast and family rooms feature a 37' vista and double bay windows

Generously sized master bedroom and three secondary bedrooms grace the second floor

4 bedrooms, 2 1/2 baths, 2-car garage

Basement foundation

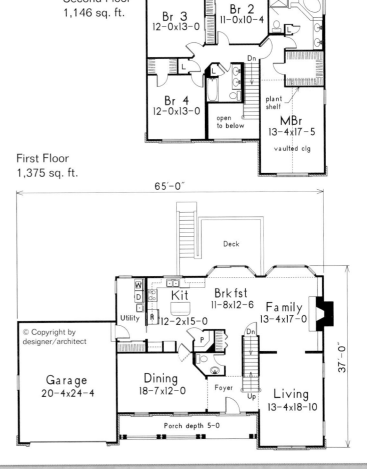

Second Floor
1,146 sq. ft.

Br 3
12-0x13-0

Br 2
11-0x10-4

Br 4
12-0x13-0

Dn

open to below

plant shelf

MBr
13-4x17-5

vaulted clg

First Floor
1,375 sq. ft.

65'-0"

Deck

W
D

Kit
12-2x15-0

Brk fst
11-8x12-6

Family
13-4x17-0

Utility

© Copyright by designer/architect

P

Dn

Garage
20-4x24-4

Dining
18-7x12-0

Foyer

Up

Living
13-4x18-10

37'-0"

Porch depth 5-0

SPECIAL FEATURES

3,181 total square feet of living area

Energy efficient home with
2" x 6" exterior walls

Located in a cheerful box-bay window,
the whirlpool tub in the master
bath is a stunning centerpiece

Triple windows brighten the great
room that can be seen from the
breakfast room/kitchen

A private and secluded study can be
used as a home office or library

4 bedrooms, 3 1/2 baths,
3-car side entry garage

Basement foundation

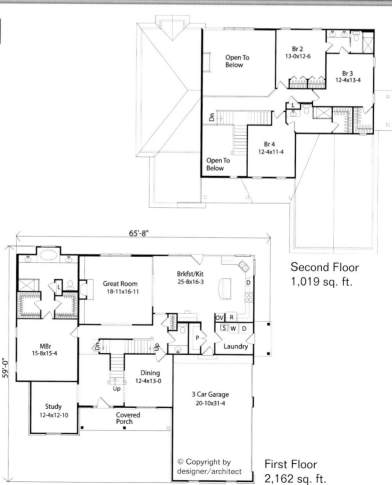

Second Floor
1,019 sq. ft.

Open To Below

Br 2
13-0x12-6

Br 3
12-4x13-4

Dn

Br 4
12-4x11-4

Open To Below

65'-8"

59'-0"

Great Room
18-11x16-11

Brkfst/Kit
25-8x16-3

MBr
15-8x15-4

Dining
12-4x13-0

Laundry

Study
12-4x12-10

Covered Porch

3 Car Garage
20-10x31-4

© Copyright by
designer/architect

First Floor
2,162 sq. ft.

SPECIAL FEATURES

3,271 total square feet of living area

The grand room features a handsome fireplace framed by French doors on either side leading out to the deck

The see-through fireplace gives the master bedroom a natural focal point

The second floor balcony overlooks the grand room

A bonus room/bedroom #5 above the garage allows for an additional 412 square feet of living area

4 bedrooms, 4 1/2 baths, 3-car side entry garage

Walk-out basement foundation

Rear View

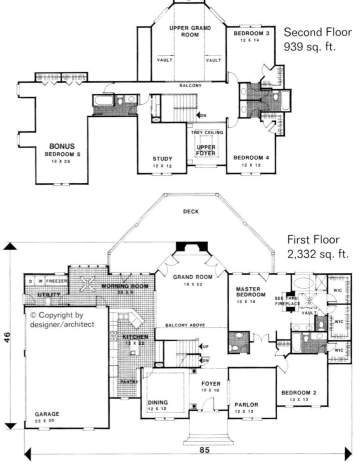

Second Floor
939 sq. ft.

UPPER GRAND ROOM

BEDROOM 3
12 X 14

VAULT   VAULT

BALCONY

BONUS
BEDROOM 5
13 X 25

STUDY
12 X 12

TREY CEILING

UPPER FOYER

BEDROOM 4
12 X 13

DECK

First Floor
2,332 sq. ft.

D W FREEZER

UTILITY

GRAND ROOM
19 X 22

MASTER BEDROOM
15 X 14

SEE THRU FIREPLACE

WIC

VAULT

WIC

MORNING ROOM
32 X 9

© Copyright by designer/architect

KITCHEN
13 X 13

BALCONY ABOVE

UP

WIC

DN

PANTRY

GARAGE
22 X 30

DINING
12 X 12

FOYER
10 X 10

PARLOR
12 X 12

BEDROOM 2
13 X 13

46

85

SPECIAL FEATURES

2,558 total square feet of living area

The garage conveniently enters the home to find the laundry room and pantry for easy unloading

Formal living and dining areas are located at the entry while the casual family room is at the rear of the house

All the bedrooms are located on the second floor and enjoy an abundance of closet space

4 bedrooms, 2 1/2 baths, 2-car garage

Basement foundation

Br2
12-0x11-5

MBr
14-0x18-8
Vaulted Clg.

Dn

Br4
11-4x12-6

Br3
11-4x12-0

Second Floor
1,274 sq. ft.

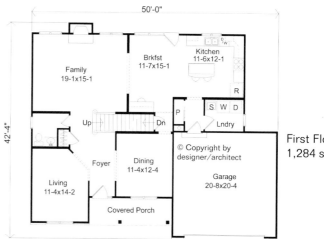

50'-0"

42'-4"

Family
19-1x15-1

Brkfst
11-7x15-1

Kitchen
11-6x12-1

R

Up

Dn

P

S W D

Lndry

© Copyright by
designer/architect

Foyer

Dining
11-4x12-4

Living
11-4x14-2

Garage
20-8x20-4

Covered Porch

First Floor
1,284 sq. ft.

SPECIAL FEATURES

- 3,072 total square feet of living area

- Master bedroom boasts a fireplace, large dressing area and a garden bath

- Kitchen includes a walk-in pantry

- Sunroom breakfast area accesses the rear porch

- Great room features a vaulted ceiling and a fireplace

- The second floor bonus room has an additional 374 square feet of living area

- 4 bedrooms, 2 1/2 baths, 2-car side entry garage

- Basement foundation

Second Floor
843 sq. ft.

Br 3
12-0x13-10

Br 4
10-4x13-0

open to below

Dn

Balcony

Optional Bonus Rm
16-4x21-0
sloped ceiling

Br 2
12-0x12-0

skylts
sloped clg

Brk fst
12-0x14-8

W D

Family
20-0x14-0
sloped ceiling

Kit
15-0x11-8

recessed ceiling

dressing

P

62'-4"

Living
16-8x15-0

Up

Foyer

Dn

© Copyright by designer/architect

Porch

Dining
12-0x14-4

MBr
15-0x20-0

Garage
21-4x24-0

First Floor
2,229 sq. ft.

60'-0"

SPECIAL FEATURES

3,882 total square feet of living area

The stately foyer is two stories tall with two guest closets and balcony overlook

A colossal-sized family room enjoys a fireplace with log bin and walk-around wet bar

A large first floor study provides a secluded retreat

Second floor balcony views family room and foyer below

4 bedrooms, 3 baths, 3-car side entry garage

Basement foundation

Second Floor
1,632 sq. ft.

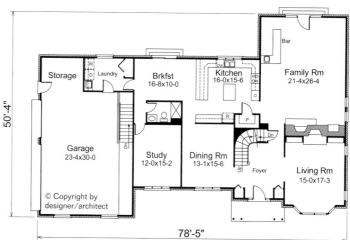

First Floor
2,250 sq. ft.

SPECIAL FEATURES

2,324 total square feet of living area

Striking exterior with stucco and hip roof

Ascending flared staircase adds drama to the open foyer with second floor balcony

Sunken two-story great room with balcony overlook is enhanced with arched transom windows and opens to an octagon-shaped breakfast room

Master suite enjoys an opulent bath overlooking a private walled garden

3 bedrooms, 2 1/2 baths, 2-car garage

Partial basement/slab foundation

Open to Great Rm Below

Balcony

Br 3
12-0x11-4

Br 2
13-4x13-9

Up

Plant Shelf

Second Floor
725 sq. ft.

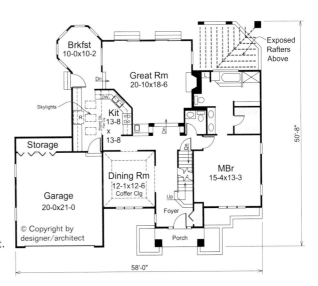

Brkfst
10-0x10-2

Great Rm
20-10x18-6

Exposed Rafters Above

Skylights

Kit
13-8
x
13-8

Dn

Dn

Dn

Storage

Dining Rm
12-1x12-6
Coffer Clg

MBr
15-4x13-3

Garage
20-0x21-0

Up

Foyer

Porch

50'-8"

58'-0"

© Copyright by designer/architect

First Floor
1,599 sq. ft.

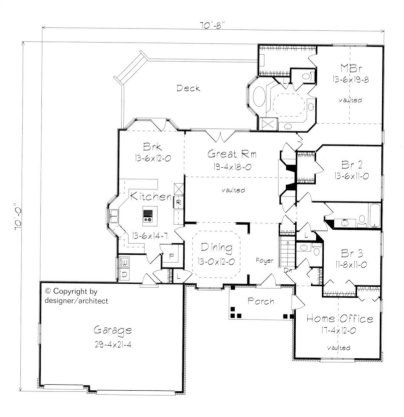

SPECIAL FEATURES

2,452 total square feet of living area

Cheery and spacious home office room with private entrance and bath, two closets, vaulted ceiling and transomed window is perfect shown as a home office or a fourth bedroom

Delightful great room features a vaulted ceiling, fireplace, extra storage closets and patio doors to sundeck

Extra-large kitchen features a walk-in pantry, cooktop island and bay window

Vaulted master bedroom includes transomed windows, walk-in closet and luxurious bath

3 bedrooms, 2 1/2 baths, 3-car garage

Basement foundation

70'-8"

70'-0"

Deck

Brk
13-6x12-0

Great Rm
19-4x18-0
vaulted

MBr
13-6x19-8
vaulted

Br 2
13-6x11-0

Kitchen
13-6x14-7

Dining
13-0x12-0

Foyer

Br 3
11-8x11-0

© Copyright by designer/architect

Porch

Garage
29-4x21-4

Home Office
17-4x12-0
vaulted

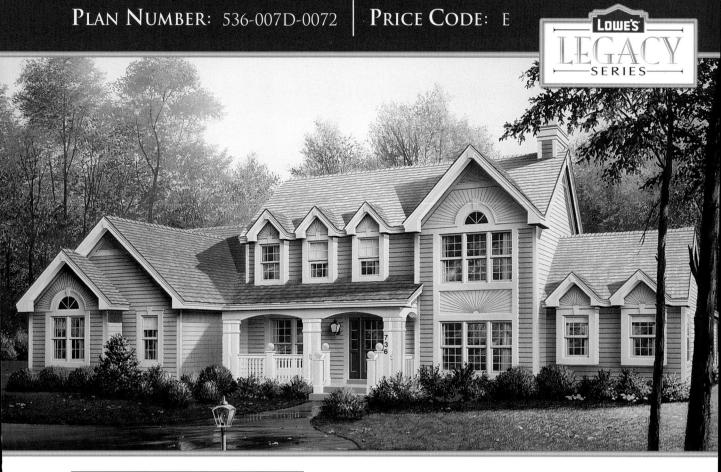

SPECIAL FEATURES

2,900 total square feet of living area

Elegant entry foyer leads to the second floor balcony overlook of the vaulted two-story atrium

Spacious kitchen features an island breakfast bar, walk-in pantry, bayed breakfast room and adjoining screened porch

Two large second floor bedrooms and stair balconies overlook a sun-drenched two-story vaulted atrium

4 bedrooms, 3 1/2 baths, 2-car side entry garage

Basement foundation

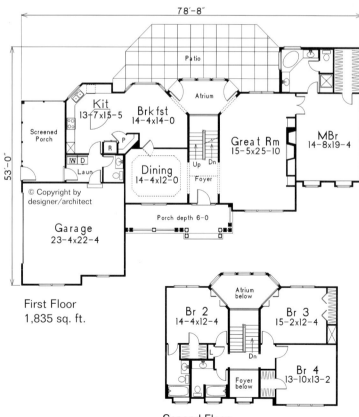

First Floor
1,835 sq. ft.

Second Floor
1,065 sq. ft.

SPECIAL FEATURES

2,602 total square feet of living area

Kitchen/dinette is joined by the family room to produce a central living space

Living and dining rooms combine for an ideal entertainment space

Master bedroom includes a private bath with an oversized step-up tub and an enormous walk-in closet

4 bedrooms, 2 1/2 baths, 3-car garage

Basement foundation

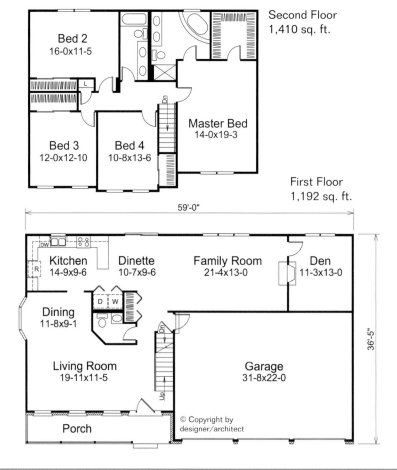

Second Floor
1,410 sq. ft.

Bed 2
16-0x11-5

Master Bed
14-0x19-3

Bed 3
12-0x12-10

Bed 4
10-8x13-6

First Floor
1,192 sq. ft.

59'-0"

Kitchen
14-9x9-6

Dinette
10-7x9-6

Family Room
21-4x13-0

Den
11-3x13-0

Dining
11-8x9-1

Living Room
19-11x11-5

Garage
31-8x22-0

36'-5"

Porch

© Copyright by designer/architect

SPECIAL FEATURES

2,760 total square feet of living area

Both secondary bedrooms on the second floor have their own full baths and large activity areas

The screened porch off the family room offers a place for outdoor relaxation

A box-bay window adds charm and character to guest bedroom #4

A centrally located elevator makes getting from one floor to another easy

4 bedrooms, 4 baths, 3 1/2-car side entry garage

Basement foundation

Second Floor
1,460 sq. ft.

© Copyright by designer/architect

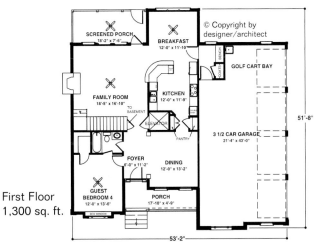

First Floor
1,300 sq. ft.

SPECIAL FEATURES

3,352 total square feet of living area

A see-through fireplace is the focal point of the spacious vaulted entry and grand sunken great room

An awesome private place for family gatherings is created by the luxurious kitchen, bayed breakfast area and morning room with fireplace

The master bedroom features a vaulted ceiling, open atrium with two-story arched window wall, balcony for sitting and a posh bath that shares a see-through fireplace

Below the master bedroom and adjacent to the atrium is an ideal room for exercise or study

3 bedrooms, 2 1/2 baths, 3-car side entry garage

Walk-out basement foundation

2,755 square feet on the first floor and 597 square feet on the lower level

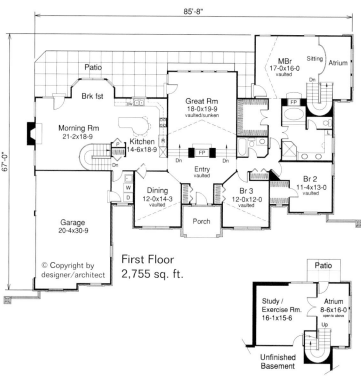

First Floor
2,755 sq. ft.

Patio

Brk fst

Morning Rm
21-2x18-9

Kitchen
14-6x18-9

Great Rm
18-0x19-9
vaulted/sunken

MBr
17-0x16-0
vaulted

Sitting

Atrium

FP

Entry
vaulted

Dining
12-0x14-3
vaulted

Br 3
12-0x12-0
vaulted

Br 2
11-4x13-0
vaulted

Porch

Garage
20-4x30-9

© Copyright by designer/architect

85'-8"

67'-0"

Lower Level
597 sq. ft.

Patio

Study / Exercise Rm.
16-1x15-6

Atrium
8-6x16-0
open to above

Up

Unfinished Basement

Up

Unfinished Basement

THE LOWE'S LEGACY SERIES
MULTI-FAMILY HOME PLANS

HDA, Inc. is proud to introduce to you the Lowe's Legacy Series. The multi-family home plans in this collection carry on the Lowe's tradition of quality and expertise, and will continue to do so for many generations.

Choosing a home plan can be a daunting task. With the Legacy Series, we will set your mind at ease. Selecting a plan from this group will ensure a home designed with the Lowe's standard of excellence, creating a dream home for you and your family.

This collection of Legacy Series plans includes our most popular multi-family home plans. Browse through the pages to discover a multi-family home with the options and special characteristics you need.

Along with one-of-a-kind craftsmanship, all Legacy Series home plans offer industry-leading material lists. These accurate material lists will save you a considerable amount of time and money, providing you with the quantity, dimensions and descriptions of the major building materials necessary to construct your home. You'll get faster and more accurate bids from your contractor while saving money by paying for only the materials you need.

The Lowe's Legacy Series is the perfect place to start your search for the home of your dreams. You will find the expected beauty you want and the functional efficiency you need, all designed with unmatched quality.

Turn the page and begin the wonderful journey of finding your new home.

Photos clockwise from top: 536-008D-0034, page 248; 536-057D-0015, page 257; 536-023D-0014, page 259; 536-007D-0076, page 246.

SPECIAL FEATURES

2,885 total square feet of living area

Cozy study adjoins the master bedroom

Several windows brighten
the main living area

Practical counterspace in the kitchen
overlooks the dining and living areas

Convenient laundry closet is
located on the second floor

Each unit has 3 bedrooms, 3 baths

Slab foundation

Unit A has 1,437 square feet
of living space and Unit B has
1,448 square feet of living space

Rear View

Unit B
Second Floor
645 sq. ft.

Balcony

MBr
14-4x13-0

MBr

Study
8-6x6-6

Study

W/D

Dn

Unit A
Second
Floor
634 sq. ft.

Br 2
10-2x10-0

Br 2

Unit B
First Floor
803 sq. ft.

Deck

Deck

Din
9-0x12-0

Living
14-6x18-0

Living

Din

39'-6"

Kit
11-6x12-6

Up

Kit

R

Unit A
First Floor
803 sq. ft.

Porch
13-0x5-0

Br 3
10-6x10-0

Br 3

48'-0"

© Copyright by designer/architect

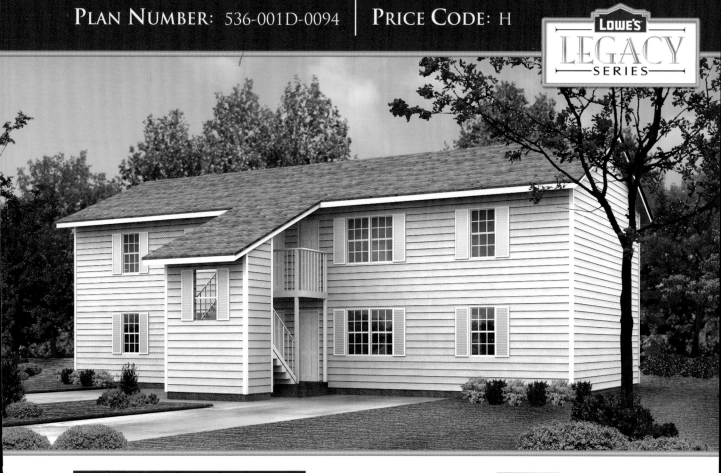

SPECIAL FEATURES

3,360 total square feet of living area

Bedrooms have ample closet space

Laundry closet is near both bedrooms

Convenient U-shaped kitchen is adjacent to the dining room with access to the deck on the first floor and balcony on the second floor

Adjacent to the living room is a handy coat and linen closet

Each unit has 2 bedrooms, 1 bath

Crawl space foundation, drawings also include slab foundation

Fourplex has 840 square feet of living space per unit

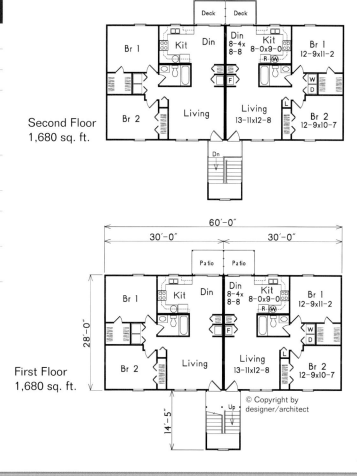

Second Floor
1,680 sq. ft.

First Floor
1,680 sq. ft.

© Copyright by designer/architect

LOWE'S LEGACY SERIES

SPECIAL FEATURES

1,704 total square feet of living area

Smartly designed layout with emphasis on efficiency

Functional kitchen embraces the sun with its bay window, glass sliding doors and pass-through to living room

Five generously designed closets offer an abundance of storage

Each unit has 2 bedrooms, 1 bath, 1-car garage

Basement foundation

Duplex has 852 square feet of living space per unit

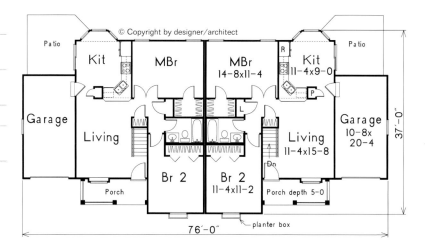

© Copyright by designer/architect

Patio

Kit

MBr

MBr 14-8x11-4

Kit 11-4x9-0

Patio

Garage

Living

Living 11-4x15-8

Garage 10-8x 20-4

Br 2

Br 2 11-4x11-2

Porch

Porch depth 5-0

planter box

76'-0"

37'-0"

Dn

SPECIAL FEATURES

- 1,044 total square feet of living area

- Easily converts to a duplex unit

- Great layout for narrow lot

- Master bedroom includes a walk-in closet, dressing area and private entrance to bath

- Convenient entrance from garage into main living area

- Kitchen includes an island cooktop, stackable washer/dryer closet and adjacent dining area with patio access

- Living room boasts a cozy corner fireplace

- Each unit has 3 bedrooms, 1 bath, 2-car garage

- Slab foundation

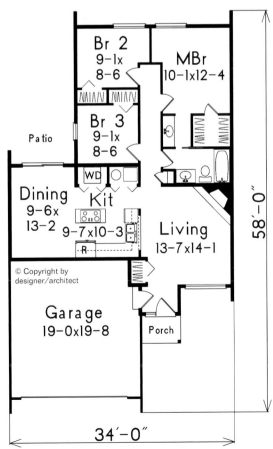

Br 2
9-1x
8-6

MBr
10-1x12-4

Patio

Br 3
9-1x
8-6

WD

Dining
9-6x
13-2

Kit
9-7x10-3

Living
13-7x14-1

© Copyright by designer/architect

R

Garage
19-0x19-8

Porch

58'-0"

34'-0"

SPECIAL FEATURES

1,352 total square feet of living area

See-through fireplace from the living room into the bedroom makes a lasting impression

Covered front porch is perfect for relaxing evenings

Galley-style kitchen is compact but well organized for efficiency

Each unit has 1 bedroom, 1 bath

Slab foundation

Duplex has 676 square feet of living space per unit

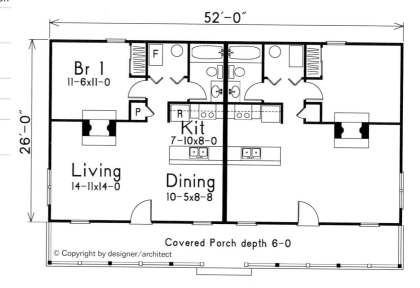

52'-0"

26'-0"

Br 1
11-6x11-0

F

P

R

Kit
7-10x8-0

Living
14-11x14-0

Dining
10-5x8-8

Covered Porch depth 6-0

LEGACY SERIES

SPECIAL FEATURES

3,056 total square feet of living area

Multiple gables, hipped roof and an elongated porch all help to create this handsome exterior

The large living room has a corner fireplace and is open to a very spacious dining area

A convenient laundry room, built-in pantry and island cabinetry are some of the many amenities of the well-equipped kitchen

Each unit has 3 bedrooms, 2 1/2 baths, 2-car garage

Crawl space foundation

Each unit has 749 square feet on the first floor and 779 square feet on the second floor with 1,528 square feet of living space per unit

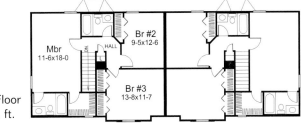

Second Floor
1,558 sq. ft.

Mbr
11-6x18-0

Br #2
9-5x12-6

HALL

Br #3
13-8x11-7

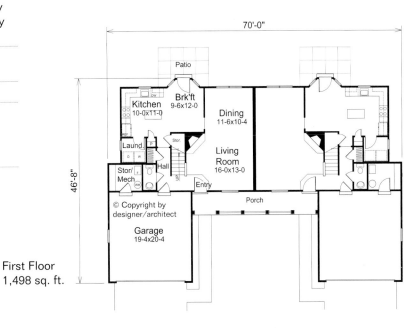

First Floor
1,498 sq. ft.

70'-0"

46'-8"

Patio

Kitchen
10-0x11-0

Brk'ft
9-6x12-0

Dining
11-6x10-4

Laund.

Stor.

Living
Room
16-0x13-0

Stor/
Mech

Hall

Entry

Porch

© Copyright by
designer/architect

Garage
19-4x20-4

LEGACY SERIES

SPECIAL FEATURES

3,666 total square feet of living area

Inviting porch and foyer lead to the vaulted living room/dining balcony with atrium window wall

Bedroom #2 doubles as a study with access to the deck through sliding glass doors

Atrium opens to the large family room and third bedroom

Each unit has 3 bedrooms, 2 baths, 2-car garage

Walk-out basement foundation

Duplex has 1,833 square feet of living space per unit

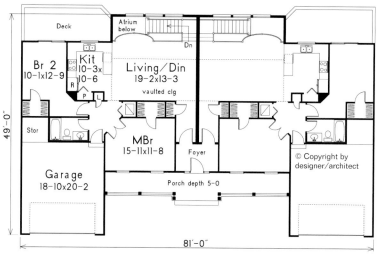

First Floor
1,073 sq. ft. per unit

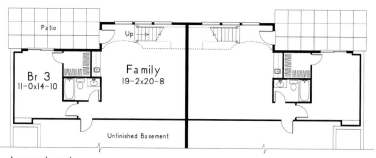

Lower Level
760 sq. ft. per unit

SPECIAL FEATURES

2,901 total square feet of living area

This fiveplex home features an extra-large porch and roof dormers that make it fit graciously into any residential neighborhood

Three first floor units have access to their own balcony while the two lower level units each enjoy private patios

Each unit has 1 bedroom, 1 bath

Walk-out basement foundation with centrally located storage and laundry room

Units A and C each have 600 square feet of living area, Unit B has 517 square feet of living area and Units D and E each have 592 square feet of living area

Fiveplex has 1,717 square feet of living area on the first floor and 1,184 square feet of living area on the lower level

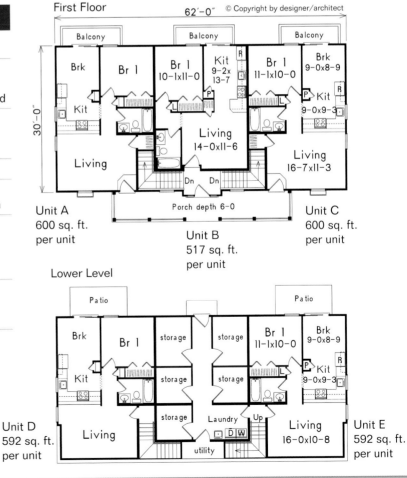

First Floor 62'-0" © Copyright by designer/architect

30'-0"

Balcony Balcony Balcony

Brk Br 1 Br 1 10-1x11-0 Kit 9-2x 13-7 Br 1 11-1x10-0 Brk 9-0x8-9

Kit Living 14-0x11-6 P Kit 9-0x9-3

Living Living 16-7x11-3

Dn Dn

Porch depth 6-0

Unit A 600 sq. ft. per unit

Unit B 517 sq. ft. per unit

Unit C 600 sq. ft. per unit

Lower Level

Patio Patio

Brk Br 1 storage storage Br 1 11-1x10-0 Brk 9-0x8-9

Kit storage storage P Kit 9-0x9-3

storage

Living storage Laundry Up Living 16-0x10-8

D W

utility

Unit D 592 sq. ft. per unit

Unit E 592 sq. ft. per unit

LEGACY SERIES

SPECIAL FEATURES

3,648 total square feet of living area

The large kitchen is adjacent to the living room

Handy linen closet in hallway

Spacious living area has easy access to patio or balcony

Centrally located laundry closet for stackable washer and dryer

Each unit has 2 bedrooms, 1 bath

Crawl space/slab foundation

Fourplex has 912 square feet of living space per unit

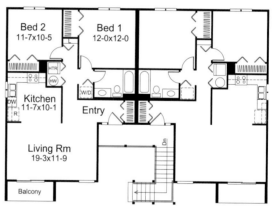

Second Floor
912 sq. ft.
per unit

Bed 2
11-7x10-5

Bed 1
12-0x12-0

Kitchen
11-7x10-1

Entry

Living Rm
19-3x11-9

Balcony

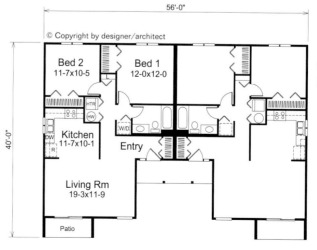

© Copyright by designer/architect

First Floor
912 sq. ft.
per unit

56'-0"

40'-0"

Bed 2
11-7x10-5

Bed 1
12-0x12-0

Kitchen
11-7x10-1

Entry

Living Rm
19-3x11-9

Patio

SPECIAL FEATURES

844 total square feet of living area

Unique design with maximum privacy for each unit featuring its own porch, breezeway entrance and large sundeck

Living room offers separate entry with closet, fireplace, sliding doors to deck and opens to dining area with bay window

The bedroom features a private bath, closet and views to porch

Each unit has 1 bedroom, 1 bath and a shared 2-car garage

Crawl space foundation

Duplex has 422 square feet of living area

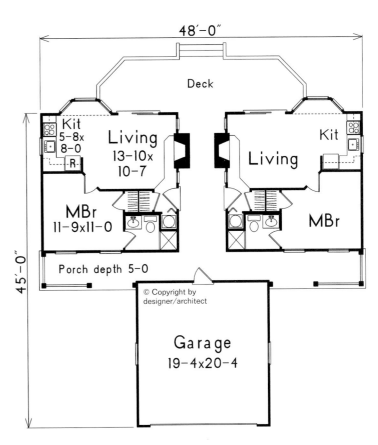

48'-0"

45'-0"

Deck

Kit
5-8x
8-0

Living
13-10x
10-7

Living

Kit

MBr
11-9x11-0

MBr

Porch depth 5-0

© Copyright by designer/architect

Garage
19-4x20-4

SPECIAL FEATURES

3,674 total square feet of living area

Spacious second floor master bedroom has a large walk-in closet

Kitchen has a snack counter which opens to the dining area and great room

Each unit has 3 bedrooms, 2 1/2 baths, 2-car garage

Basement foundation, drawings also include crawl space/slab foundation

Duplex has 1,837 total square feet of living space per unit

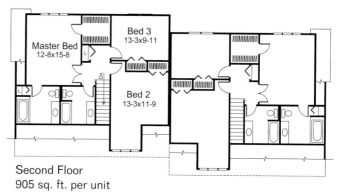

Master Bed
12-8x15-8

Bed 3
13-3x9-11

Bed 2
13-3x11-9

Second Floor
905 sq. ft. per unit

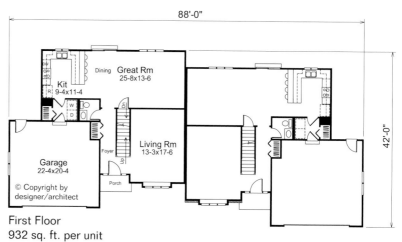

88'-0"

42'-0"

Dining   Great Rm
25-8x13-6

Kit
9-4x11-4

Living Rm
13-3x17-6

Foyer

Garage
22-4x20-4

© Copyright by
designer/architect

Porch

First Floor
932 sq. ft. per unit

SPECIAL FEATURES

2,318 total square feet of living area

Great room and dining area
are complemented with a
fireplace and patio access

Breakfast bar has a corner sink
which overlooks the great room

Plant shelf graces vaulted entry

Master bedroom provides
walk-in closet and private bath

Each unit has 3 bedrooms,
2 baths, 1-car garage

Basement foundation

Duplex has 1,159 square feet
of living space per unit

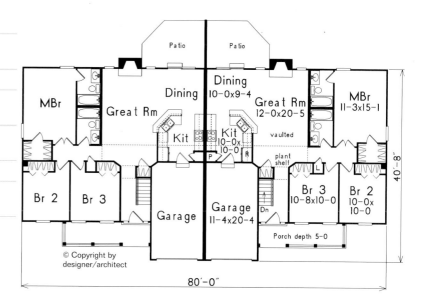

Patio   Patio

Dining
10-0x9-4

Dining

MBr   Great Rm   Great Rm   MBr
                         12-0x20-5   11-3x15-1
             Kit   Kit
                    10-0x
                    10-0   vaulted
                          plant
                          shelf

Br 2   Br 3   Br 3   Br 2
                          10-8x10-0 10-0x
                                     10-0

Garage Garage
        11-4x20-4   Dn

                    Porch depth 5-0

40'-8"

© Copyright by
designer/architect

80'-0"

SPECIAL FEATURES

1,938 total square feet of living area

The large living room is open to the kitchen and features an entry foyer with convenient coat closet

Glass sliding doors with a view of the side fenced patio, a snack bar and built-in pantry are some of the great bonuses found in the kitchen

A laundry closet with stacked washer/ dryer is located at the end of the hall that accesses the bath, linen closet and three bedrooms

Each unit has 3 bedrooms, 1 bath

Slab foundation

Each unit has 969 total square feet of living area

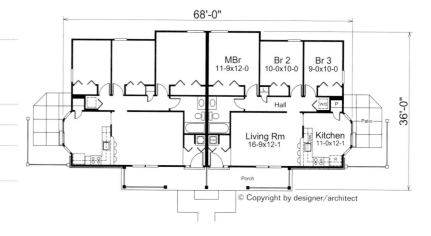

68'-0"

36'-0"

MBr
11-9x12-0

Br 2
10-0x10-0

Br 3
9-0x10-0

Hall

Patio

Living Rm
16-9x12-1

Kitchen
11-0x12-1

Porch

© Copyright by designer/architect

SPECIAL FEATURES

4,240 total square feet of living area

Kitchen, brightened by a large bay window, accesses patio on first floor units and deck on second floor units

Corner fireplace provides warmth and charm

Bedrooms are separated from living areas for privacy

Laundry is located off hall for accessibility

Each unit has 3 bedrooms, 2 baths, 1-car garage

Basement foundation

Fourplex has 1,060 square feet of living space per unit

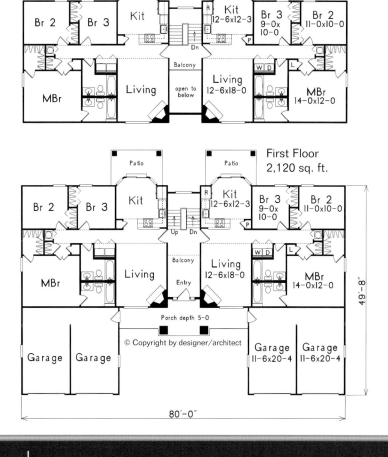

Second Floor
2,120 sq. ft.

First Floor
2,120 sq. ft.

© Copyright by designer/architect

SPECIAL FEATURES

1,924 total square feet of living area

Large bedrooms have plenty of closet space

Unit A features ranch-style living and has 792 total square feet of living area

Unit B is a 1 1/2 story and has 1,132 square feet of living area with 575 square feet on the first floor and 557 square feet on the second floor

Unit A has 2 bedrooms, 1 bath

Unit B has 2 bedrooms, 1 1/2 baths

Basement foundation

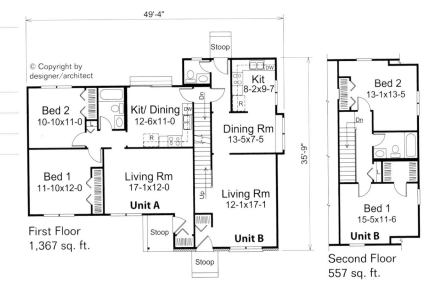

49'-4"

© Copyright by designer/architect

Bed 2
10-10x11-0

Kit/ Dining
12-6x11-0

Stoop

Kit
8-2x9-7

Dining Rm
13-5x7-5

35'-9"

Bed 2
13-1x13-5

Bed 1
11-10x12-0

Living Rm
17-1x12-0

Unit A

Living Rm
12-1x17-1

Bed 1
15-5x11-6

Unit B

First Floor
1,367 sq. ft.

Stoop

Stoop

Unit B

Second Floor
557 sq. ft.

SPECIAL FEATURES

1,200 total square feet of living area

This duplex has an L-shaped kitchen that is open to a pleasant breakfast area

The bedroom includes plenty of closetspace and access to a covered or optional screen porch

The kitchen includes space for a stacked washer and dryer

Each unit has a total of 600 square feet and a bonus room

Each unit has 1 bedroom, 1 bath, 1-car garage

Crawl space foundation

© Copyright by designer/architect

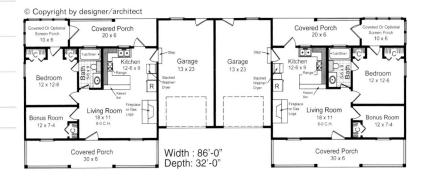

Width : 86'-0"
Depth: 32'-0"

SPECIAL FEATURES

4,936 total square feet of living area

All units have convenient rear access to the patio

Unit A has 2 bedrooms, 1 bath

Unit B has 3 bedrooms, 1 bath

Basement foundation, drawings also include crawl space/slab foundation

Unit A has 1,040 square feet of living space and Unit B has 1,428 square feet of living space with 714 square feet on both floors

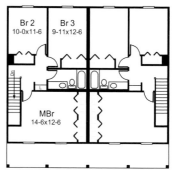

Second Floor
Unit B
714 sq. ft.
per unit

Second Floor plan rooms: Br 2 10-0x11-6, Br 3 9-11x12-6, MBr 14-6x12-6

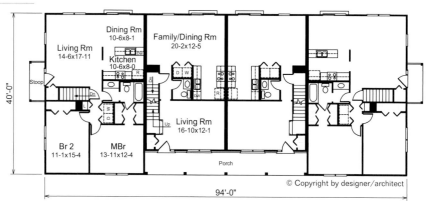

First Floor plan rooms: Living Rm 14-6x17-11, Dining Rm 10-6x8-1, Kitchen 10-6x8-0, Br 2 11-1x15-4, MBr 13-11x12-4, Family/Dining Rm 20-2x12-5, Living Rm 16-10x12-1, Stoop, Porch. Dimensions 40'-0" and 94'-0".

First Floor
Unit A
1,040 sq. ft.
per unit

First Floor
Unit B
714 sq. ft.
per unit

SPECIAL FEATURES

1,626 total square feet of living area

Energy efficient home with
2" x 6" exterior walls

Each unit features a lovely front
porch that enters to find a coat
closet and spacious living room

The large eat-in kitchen offers plenty of
space for dining and accesses the side yard

The full bath includes a
double-bowl vanity for ease of sharing

Each unit has 2 bedrooms, 1 bath

Slab foundation

Duplex has 813 square feet
of living space per unit

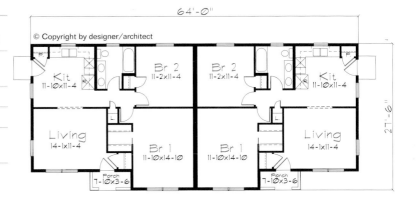

64'-0"

© Copyright by designer/architect

Kit
11-10x11-4

Br 2
11-2x11-4

Br 2
11-2x11-4

Kit
11-10x11-4

Living
14-1x11-4

Br 1
11-10x14-10

Br 1
11-10x14-10

Living
14-1x11-4

Porch
7-10x3-6

Porch
7-10x3-6

27'-6"

LEGACY SERIES

SPECIAL FEATURES

2,010 total square feet of living area

Floor plan includes plenty of storage space

Cozy family room is adjacent to the kitchen and large living room

Both units have 2 bedrooms, 1 bath, 1-car garage

Basement foundation, drawings also include crawl space/slab foundation

Duplex has 1,005 square feet of living space per unit

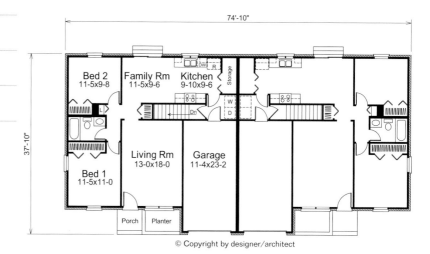

74'-10"

37'-10"

Bed 2
11-5x9-8

Family Rm
11-5x9-6

Kitchen
9-10x9-6

Storage

Living Rm
13-0x18-0

Garage
11-4x23-2

Bed 1
11-5x11-0

Porch   Planter

SPECIAL FEATURES

4,184 total square feet of living area

Combined kitchen, living and dining rooms create an open living atmosphere

Handy laundry room and large linen closet on the second floor

Master bedroom includes a private bath and balcony

First floor bedroom is an ideal guest room

Each unit has 4 bedrooms, 3 baths

Slab foundation

Duplex has 2,092 square feet of living space per unit with 1,108 square feet on the first floor and 984 square feet on the second floor

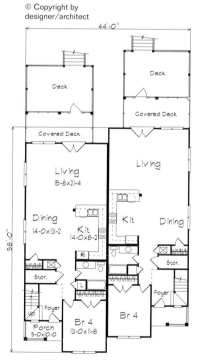

© Copyright by designer/architect

44'-0"

58'-0"

First Floor
1,108 sq. ft. per unit

Second Floor
984 sq. ft. per unit

SPECIAL FEATURES

896 total square feet of living area

Energy efficient home with
2" x 6" exterior walls

Small cabin duplex is well suited for
rental property or permanent residence

Compact, yet convenient floor plan

Well organized for economical construction

1 bedroom, 1 bath

Slab foundation

Duplex has 448 square feet
of living space per unit

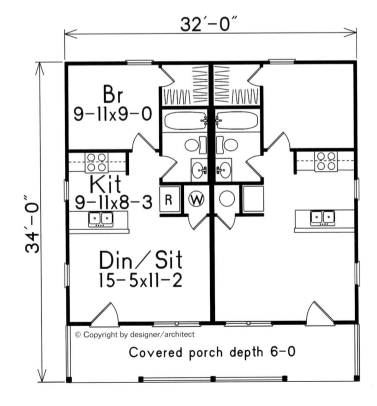

32'-0"

34'-0"

Br
9-11x9-0

Kit
9-11x8-3

Din/Sit
15-5x11-2

© Copyright by designer/architect

Covered porch depth 6-0

SPECIAL FEATURES

1,536 total square feet of living area

Living room joins the kitchen/dining area for an open atmosphere

L-shaped kitchen with outdoor access and convenient laundry area

Linen and coat closet

Each unit has 2 bedrooms, 1 bath

Crawl space foundation, drawings also include slab foundation

Duplex has 768 total square feet of living space per unit

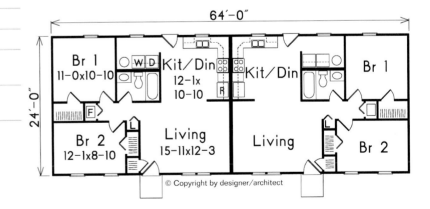

64'-0"

24'-0"

Br 1
11-0x10-10

W D

Kit/Din
12-1x
10-10

R

Kit/Din

Br 1

F

Br 2
12-1x8-10

L

Living
15-11x12-3

Living

L

Br 2

LEGACY SERIES

SPECIAL FEATURES

2,986 total square feet of living area

Beautiful stonework with planter boxes and large country porch provide a dazzling exterior

First floor units have access to their own sundecks while lower level units each enjoy a private patio

Each unit features a hookup for a stacked washer and dryer

Units A and B have 2 bedrooms, 1 bath and Units C and D have 1 bedroom, 1 bath

Walk-out basement foundation with centrally located storage area

Fourplex has 1,574 square feet of living area on the first floor and 1,412 square feet of living area on the lower level

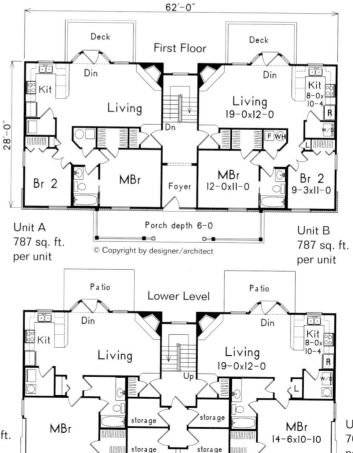

First Floor
62'-0"
28'-0"

Deck — Din — Kit — Living — Br 2 — MBr — Foyer
Deck — Din — Kit — Living 19-0x12-0 — MBr 12-0x11-0 — Br 2 9-3x11-0
Dn

Unit A
787 sq. ft.
per unit

Porch depth 6-0

Unit B
787 sq. ft.
per unit

Lower Level

Patio — Din — Kit — Living — MBr — storage
Patio — Din — Kit 8-0x10-4 — Living 19-0x12-0 — MBr 14-6x10-10 — storage
Up

Unit C
706 sq. ft.
per unit

Unit D
706 sq. ft.
per unit

SPECIAL FEATURES

7,372 total square feet of living area

Units A and D feature living/ dining combination and master bedroom retreat with lower level family room and third bedroom

Units A and D include 3 bedrooms, 3 baths, 2-car garage in a ranch plan with 1,707 square feet of living area with 1,149 on the first floor and 558 on the lower level

Units B and C feature luxurious living area and second floor with spacious master bedroom featuring two walk-in closets and a lavish bath

Units B and C include 3 bedrooms, 2 1/2 baths, 2-car garage in a two-story plan with 1,979 square feet of living area with 1,055 on the first floor and 924 on the second floor

Basement foundation

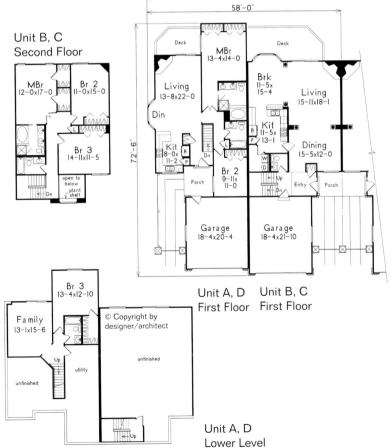

Unit B, C
Second Floor

MBr
12-0x17-0

Br 2
11-0x15-0

Br 3
14-11x11-5

open to below
plant shelf

Dn

116'-0"

58'-0"

72'-6"

Deck

Deck

MBr
13-4x14-0

Living
13-8x22-0

Din

Kit
8-0x
11-2

Brk
11-5x
15-4

Living
15-11x18-1

Kit
11-5x
13-1

Dining
15-5x12-0

Br 2
9-11x
11-0

Porch

Entry

Porch

Garage
18-4x20-4

Garage
18-4x21-10

Unit A, D
First Floor

Unit B, C
First Floor

Br 3
13-4x12-10

Family
13-1x15-6

Up

utility

unfinished

© Copyright by designer/architect

unfinished

Up

Unit A, D
Lower Level

LEGACY SERIES

SPECIAL FEATURES

2,830 total square feet of living area

Energy efficient home with
2" x 6" exterior walls

Great room, master bedroom and
dining room access covered porch

Master bedroom features a
double-door entry, walk-in closet
and private bath with shower

Great room has a fireplace and wet bar

U-shaped kitchen opens to dining room

Laundry room with plenty of
workspace conveniently accesses
the outdoors, garage and kitchen

Each unit has 2 bedrooms,
2 baths, 2-car garage

Basement foundation

Duplex has 1,415 square feet
of living space per unit

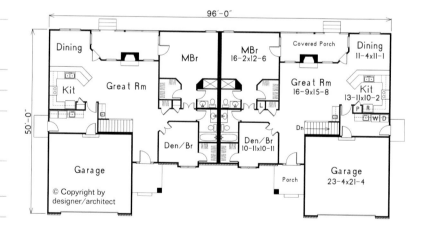

96'-0"

50'-0"

Dining

MBr

MBr
16-2x12-6

Covered Porch

Dining
11-4x11-1

Kit

Great Rm

Great Rm
16-9x15-8

Kit
13-11x10-2

Den/Br

Den/Br
10-11x10-11

Dn

Garage

© Copyright by
designer/architect

Porch

Garage
23-4x21-4

W D

P R L

SPECIAL FEATURES

2,662 total square feet of living area

Living room has a vaulted ceiling, built-in bookshelves and a fireplace

Plenty of storage space is offered in this duplex

Each unit has 2 bedrooms, 2 baths, 2-car garage

Large bedroom with a private bath and two closets is an ideal master suite

Basement foundation, drawings also include crawl space/slab foundation

Duplex has 1,331 square feet of living space per unit

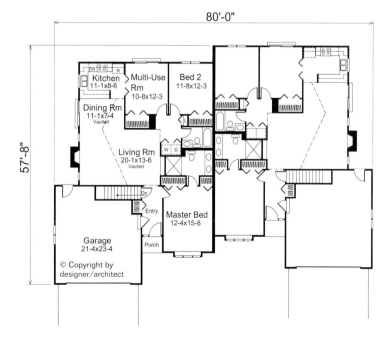

SPECIAL FEATURES

1,700 total square feet of living area

Front facade fits splendidly with residential surroundings

Well-planned kitchen includes an abundance of cabinets

Spacious bedroom with double closets

Plant shelf, open stairway and vaulted ceilings highlight living space

Convenient entrance from garage into main living area

Dining room accesses deck

Each unit has 2 bedrooms, 1 bath, 1-car side entry garage

Basement foundation

Duplex has 850 square feet of living space per unit

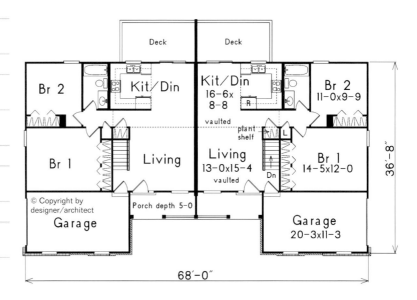

SPECIAL FEATURES

3,258 total square feet of living area

Multi-gables, brickwork, windows with shutters and planter boxes create great curb appeal

Living room includes a large dining area, fireplace, entry with coat closet and nearby powder room

Well-equipped kitchen includes an island snack bar, bayed breakfast room, built-in pantry, corner windows above sink and laundry room

Second floor has large bedrooms including a vaulted master bedroom with luxury bath

Each unit has 3 bedrooms, 2 1/2 baths, 2-car garage

Basement foundation

Duplex has 1,629 square feet of living space per unit

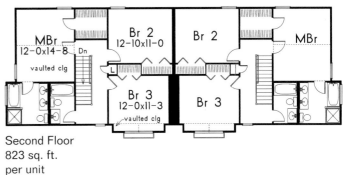

Second Floor
823 sq. ft.
per unit

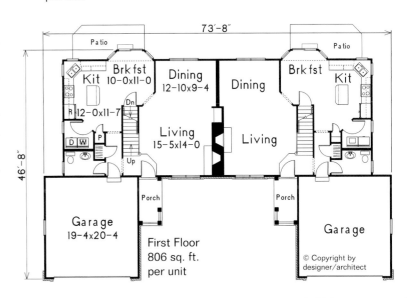

First Floor
806 sq. ft.
per unit

© Copyright by
designer/architect

SPECIAL FEATURES

2,800 total square feet of living area

Energy efficient home with
2" x 6" exterior walls

Large master bedroom enjoys a walk-in
closet and private bath with linen area

Covered entrance opens into
entry with coat closet

Work area in garage

Convenient laundry room

Half wall defines the kitchen and
opens to the large living room

Each unit has 2 bedrooms,
2 baths, 2-car garage

Basement foundation

Duplex has 1,400 square feet
of living space per unit

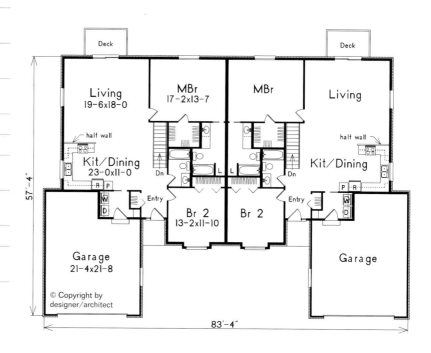

Deck

Living
19-6x18-0

MBr
17-2x13-7

MBr

Living

half wall

half wall

Kit/Dining
23-0x11-0

Dn

L   L

Dn

Kit/Dining

57'-4"

R P

Entry

Br 2
13-2x11-10

Br 2

Entry

P R

W
D

W
D

Garage
21-4x21-8

Garage

© Copyright by
designer/architect

83'-4"

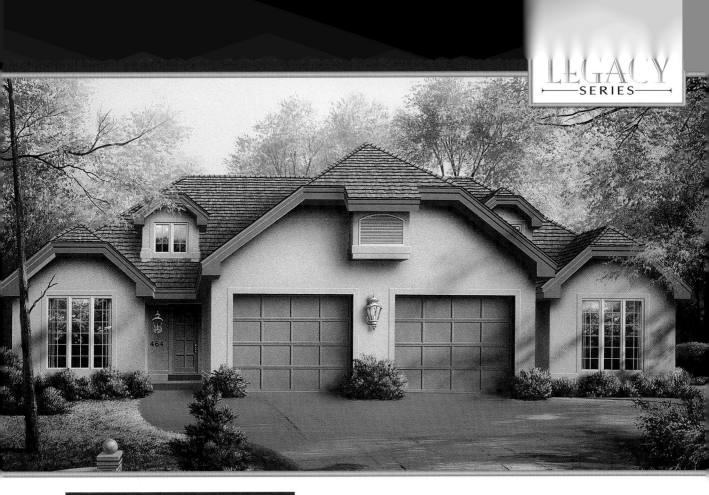

SPECIAL FEATURES

1,992 total square feet of living area

Graciously designed ranch duplex
with alluring openness

Vaulted kitchen with accent on spaciousness
features huge pantry, plenty of cabinets
and convenient laundry room

Master bedroom includes its own cozy
bath and oversized walk-in closet

Each unit has 2 bedrooms,
2 baths, 1-car garage

Basement foundation

Duplex has 996 square feet
of living space per unit

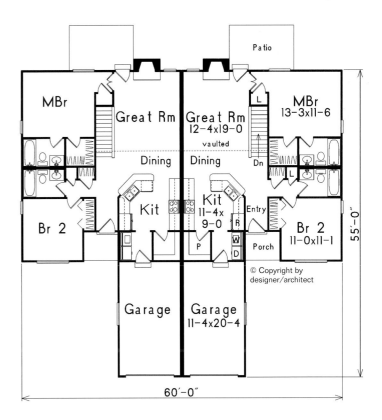

Patio

MBr

Great Rm | Great Rm
12-4x19-0
vaulted

MBr
13-3x11-6

Dining | Dining

Dn

Kit | Kit
11-4x
9-0

Entry

Br 2 | Br 2
11-0x11-1

Porch

55'-0"

© Copyright by
designer/architect

Garage | Garage
11-4x20-4

60'-0"

SPECIAL FEATURES

2,830 total square feet of living area

Great room, master bedroom and dining room access covered porch

Master bedroom features a double-door entry, walk-in closet and private bath with shower

Great room has a fireplace and wet bar

U-shaped kitchen opens to the dining room

Laundry room with plenty of workspace conveniently accesses the outdoors, garage and kitchen

2" x 6" exterior walls available, please order plan #536-058D-0071

Each unit has 2 bedrooms, 2 baths, 2-car garage

Basement foundation

Duplex has 1,415 square feet of living space per unit

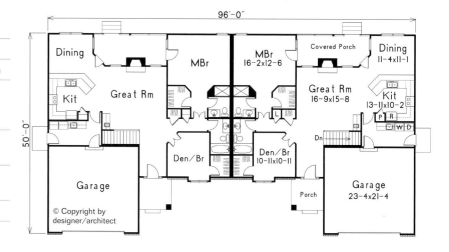

© Copyright by designer/architect

SPECIAL FEATURES

2,840 total square feet of living area

Living room is graced with a
bay window and fireplace

Kitchen offers efficient layout
and overlooks dining area

Bedroom includes a spacious walk-in closet

Convenient laundry closet is located off hall

First floor units have patios and second floor
units have decks located off the dining area

Each unit has 1 bedroom, 1 bath

Basement foundation

Fourplex has 710 square feet
of living space per unit

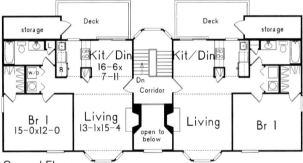

Second Floor
1,420 sq. ft.

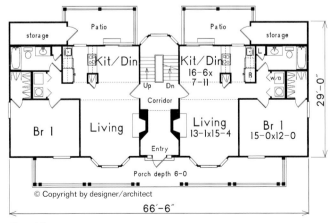

© Copyright by designer/architect

First Floor
1,420 sq. ft.

SPECIAL FEATURES

1,966 total square feet of living area

Energy efficient home with
2" x 6" exterior walls

Entry opens into main living
space or dining area/kitchen

Ample closet/storage space
throughout duplex

Large L-shaped dining
area/kitchen has garage access

Several windows brighten the living room

Each unit has 2 bedrooms,
1 bath, 1-car garage

Basement foundation

Duplex has 983 square feet
of living space per unit

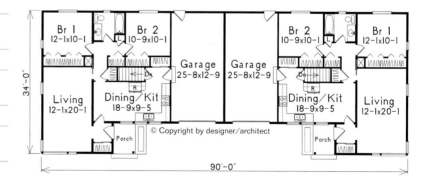

© Copyright by designer/architect

SPECIAL FEATURES

1,966 total square feet of living area

Lots of storage space throughout

Oversized kitchen is easy to organize

Large living room windows
allow plenty of sunlight

Each unit has 3 bedrooms, 1 bath

Basement foundation, drawings also
include crawl space/slab foundation

Duplex has 983 square feet
of living space per unit

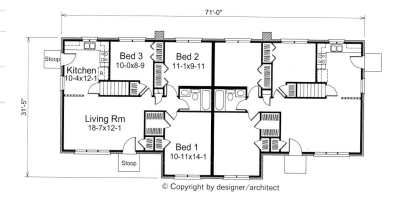

71'-0"

31'-5"

Stoop

Kitchen
10-4x12-1

Bed 3
10-0x8-9

Bed 2
11-1x9-11

Living Rm
18-7x12-1

Bed 1
10-11x14-1

Stoop

SPECIAL FEATURES

1,536 total square feet of living area

Living room joins the kitchen/dining area for an open atmosphere

L-shaped kitchen has outdoor access and a convenient laundry area

Handy linen and coat closet

Welcoming covered front porch

Each unit has 2 bedrooms, 1 bath

Crawl space foundation, drawings also include slab foundation

Duplex has 768 total square feet of living space per unit

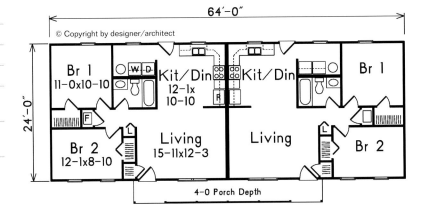

64'-0"

© Copyright by designer/architect

Br 1
11-0x10-10

W D

Kit/Din
12-1x
10-10

R

Br 1

24'-0"

F

Br 2
12-1x8-10

Living
15-11x12-3

Living

Br 2

4-0 Porch Depth

SPECIAL FEATURES

2,986 total square feet of living area

Vaulted great room, kitchen and two balconies define architectural drama

First floor master bedroom boasts a lavish bath and double walk-in closets

Impressive second floor features two large bedrooms, spacious closets, hall bath and balcony overlook

Each unit has 3 bedrooms, 2 1/2 baths, 2-car garage

Basement foundation

Duplex has 1,493 square feet of living space per unit

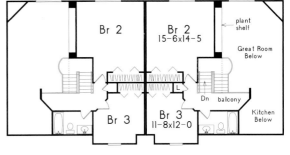

Second Floor
533 sq. ft.
per unit

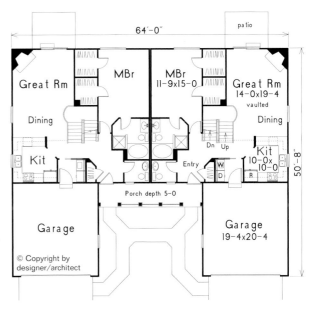

First Floor
960 sq. ft.
per unit

SPECIAL FEATURES

1,076 total square feet of living area

A country porch for quiet times leads to a living room with fireplace, dining area and efficient kitchenette

The bedroom offers a double-door entry, walk-in closet and a bath with linen closet

Spacious and private screen porch is steps away from the dining area through sliding doors

Each unit has 1 bedroom, 1 bath

Crawl space foundation, drawings also include slab foundation

Duplex has 538 square feet of living space per unit

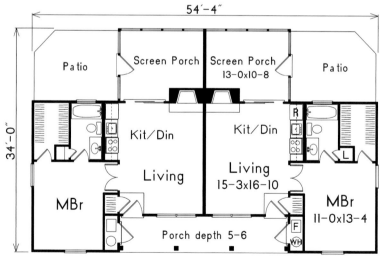

54'-4"

34'-0"

Patio

Screen Porch

Screen Porch
13-0x10-8

Patio

Kit/Din

Kit/Din

Living

Living
15-3x16-10

MBr

MBr
11-0x13-4

Porch depth 5-6

SPECIAL FEATURES

3,066 total square feet of living area

Master bedroom has a private bath, sitting area, walk-in closet and access outdoors

Kitchen has a vaulted ceiling and a snack counter that overlooks the living room

Roomy living room enjoys a fireplace, vaulted ceiling and access to deck

Each unit has 3 bedrooms, 2 baths, 2-car garage

Basement foundation, drawings also include partial basement/crawl space foundation

Duplex has 1,533 square feet of living space per unit

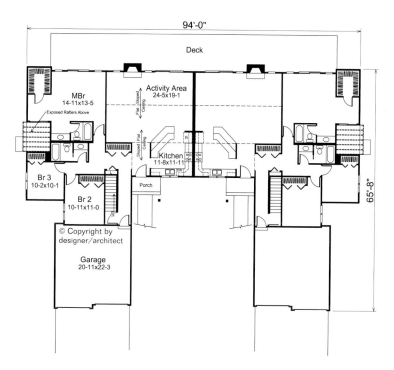

94'-0"

Deck

MBr
14-11x13-5

Exposed Rafters Above

Activity Area
24-5x19-1

Flat Sloped Ceiling

Sloped Flat Ceiling

Kitchen
11-8x11-11

Br 3
10-2x10-1

Porch

Br 2
10-11x11-0

© Copyright by
designer/architect

Garage
20-11x22-3

65'-8"

SPECIAL FEATURES

3,502 total square feet of living area

Two-story entry has an elegant staircase that leads to the living room with a fireplace

Breakfast room enjoys a bay window, sliding glass doors to outdoor balcony and a pass-through to the kitchen

A lower level laundry area is provided in each unit

Each unit has 3 bedrooms, 2 1/2 baths, 2-car drive under garage

Walk-out basement foundation

Duplex has 1,751 square feet of living space per unit and 252 square feet on the lower level

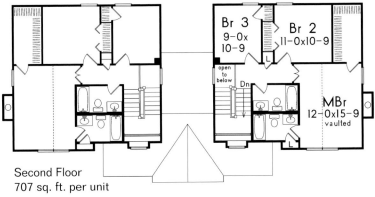

Second Floor
707 sq. ft. per unit

Br 3
9-0x 10-9

Br 2
11-0x10-9

open to below

Dn

MBr
12-0x15-9
vaulted

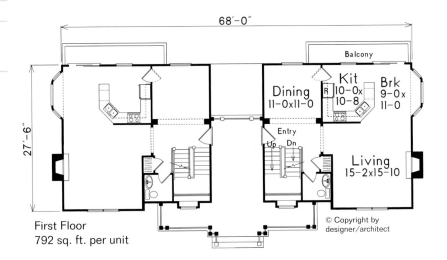

First Floor
792 sq. ft. per unit

68'-0"

27'-6"

Balcony

Dining
11-0x11-0

Kit
10-0x 10-8

Brk
9-0x 11-0

Entry
Up   Dn

Living
15-2x15-10

SPECIAL FEATURES

3,604 total square feet of living area

Large storage closet is located in the hallway

Galley-type kitchen overlooks
the living and dining rooms

All units have a spacious and handy
utility room with side entrance

Dining and living rooms combine
for spaciousness

Each unit has 2 bedrooms, 1 bath

Shallow basement foundation

Fourplex has 901 square feet
of living space per unit

51'-0"

Br 1
13-1x11-0

Br 2
9-1x11-0

Dn

W D WH

Utility

F

38'-0"

R

Kit
8-8x
10-0

Living Rm
12-2x17-9

Up Dn

Dining Rm
8-8x7-9

Landing

© Copyright by designer/architect

Stoop

SPECIAL FEATURES

2,408 total square feet of living area

The large great room offers a fireplace and dining area with view of the patio

Each unit enjoys its own private garage, front porch and rear patio

The second floor bedrooms are large in size and feature spacious walk-in closets

Each unit has 2 bedrooms, 1 1/2 baths, 1-car garage

Basement foundation

Duplex has 1,204 square feet of living space per unit

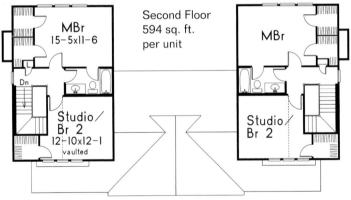

Second Floor
594 sq. ft.
per unit

MBr
15-5x11-6

Dn

Studio/
Br 2
12-10x12-1
vaulted

MBr

Studio/
Br 2

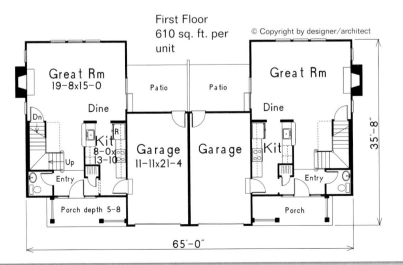

First Floor
610 sq. ft. per
unit

© Copyright by designer/architect

Great Rm
19-8x15-0

Dine

Patio

Patio

Dine

Great Rm

Dn

Up

Kit
8-0x
13-10

R

Garage
11-11x21-4

Garage

Kit

Entry

Entry

Porch depth 5-8

Porch

35'-8"

65'-0"

Lowe's Special Rebate Offer

Purchase any plan package featured in this book PLUS at least $15,000 of your materials from Lowe's and receive a gift card for the purchase price of your plans.

To receive the rebate:

1. Purchase any of the plan packages in this publication PLUS at least $15,000 of the materials to build your home at Lowe's before 12/31/10. Requests must be postmarked by 1/31/11. Claims postmarked after this date will not be honored.

2. Limit one gift card per set of plans.

3. Please allow 3-4 weeks for processing. If you do not receive a gift card after 4 weeks, visit www.lowes.com/rebates, or you may call 1-877-204-1223.

4. Please keep a copy of all materials submitted for your records.

5. Copy the entire sale receipt(s), including store name, location, purchase date, and invoice number, showing blueprint purchase and total amount spent.

6. Mail this complete page with your name, address and other information below, along with a copy of the receipt(s).

Name _____

Street Address _____

City _____

State/Zip _____

Daytime phone number (_____) - _____

E-mail address _____

Plan number purchased 536- _____

I purchased a
☐ One-Set Plan Package
☐ Five-Set Plan Package
☐ Eight-Set Plan Package
☐ Reproducible Masters
☐ Builder's CAD Package

MAIL TO:
Lowe's Free Gift Card Offer
P.O. Box 3029
Young America, MN 55558-3029

Check the status of your rebate at www.lowes.com/rebates

Our Blueprint Packages Include...

Quality plans for building your future, with extras that provide unsurpassed value, ensure good construction and long-term enjoyment.

Cover Sheet

Included with many of the plans, the cover sheet is the artist's rendering of the exterior of the home. It will give you an idea of how your home will look when completed and landscaped.

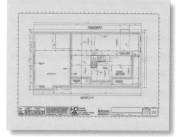

Foundation

The foundation plan shows the layout of the basement, walk-out basement, crawl space, slab or pier foundation. All necessary notations and dimensions are included. See plan page for the foundation types included. If the home plan you choose does not have your desired foundation type, our Customer Service Representatives can advise you on how to customize your foundation to suit your specific needs or site conditions.

Floor Plans

The floor plans show the placement of walls, doors, closets, plumbing fixtures, electrical outlets, columns, and beams for each level of the home.

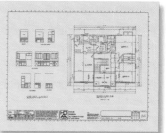

Interior Elevations

Interior elevations provide views of special interior elements such as fireplaces, kitchen cabinets, built-in units and other features of the home.

Exterior Elevations

Exterior elevations illustrate the front, rear and both sides of the house, with all details of exterior materials and the required dimensions.

Sections

Show detail views of the home or portions of the home as if it were sliced from the roof to the foundation. This sheet shows important areas such as load-bearing walls, stairs, joists, trusses and other structural elements, which are critical for proper construction.

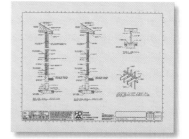

Details

Show how to construct certain components of your home, such as the roof system, stairs, deck, etc.

Now that you've found the home you've been looking for, here are some suggestions on how to make your Dream Home a reality. To get started, order the type of plans that fit your particular situation.

YOUR CHOICES

THE ONE-SET STUDY PACKAGE -

We offer a One-set plan package so you can study your home in detail. This one set is considered a study set and is marked "not for construction." It is a copyright violation to reproduce blueprints.

THE MINIMUM 5-SET PACKAGE -

If you're ready to start the construction process, this 5-set package is the minimum number of blueprint sets you will need. It will require keeping close track of each set so they can be used by multiple subcontractors and tradespeople.

THE STANDARD 8-SET PACKAGE -

For best results in terms of cost, schedule and quality of construction, we recommend you order eight (or more) sets of blueprints. Besides one set for yourself, additional sets of blueprints will be required by your mortgage lender, local building department, general contractor and all subcontractors working on foundation, electrical, plumbing, heating/air conditioning, carpentry work, etc.

REPRODUCIBLE MASTERS -

If you wish to make some minor design changes, you'll want to order reproducible masters. These drawings contain the same information as the blueprints but are printed on reproducible paper and clearly indicates your right to alter, copy or reproduce. This will allow your builder or a local design professional to make the necessary drawing changes without the major expense of redrawing the plans. This package also allows you to print copies of the modified plans as needed. The right of building only one structure from these plans is licensed exclusively to the buyer. You may not use this design to build a second or multiple dwelling(s) without purchasing another blueprint. Each violation of the Copyright Law is punishable in a fine.

MIRROR REVERSE SETS -

Plans can be printed in mirror reverse. These plans are useful when the house would fit your site better if all the rooms were on the opposite side than shown. They are simply a mirror image of the original drawings causing the lettering and dimensions to read backwards. Therefore, when ordering mirror reverse drawings, you must purchase at least one set of right-reading plans. Some of our plans are offered mirror reverse right-reading. This means the plan, lettering and dimensions are flipped but read correctly. See the Home Plans Index on pages 285-286 for availability

CAD PACKAGES -

A CAD package is a complete set of construction drawings in an electronic file format. They are beneficial if you have a significant amount of changes to make to the home plan or if you need to make the home plan fit your local codes. If you purchase a CAD Package, you can take the plan to a local design professional who uses AutoCAD or DataCAD and they can modify the design much quicker than with a paper-based drawing, which will help save you time and money. Just like our reproducible masters, with a CAD package you will receive a one-time build copyright release that allows you to make changes and the necessary copies needed to build your home. For more information and availability, please call our Customer Service Department at 1-877-379-3420.

PDF FILE FORMAT -

A complete set of construction drawings in an electronic format that allows you to modify and reproduce the plans to fit your needs. Since these are electronic files, we can send them to you within 24 hours (Mon-Fri, 8-5 CST) via email and save you shipping costs. They also offer printing flexibility by allowing you to print the size and number of sets you need. Note: These are not CAD files and cannot be altered electronically.

Your Blueprint Package will contain the necessary construction information to build your home. We also offer the following products and services to save you time and money in the building process.

MATERIAL LIST

Material lists are available for all of the plans in this book. Each list gives you the quantity, dimensions and description of the building materials necessary to construct your home. You'll get faster and more accurate bids from your contractor while saving money by paying for only the materials you need. See your Commercial Sales Specialist at your local Lowe's Store to receive a free take-off.

EXPRESS DELIVERY

Most orders are processed within 24 hours of receipt. Please allow 7-10 business days for delivery. If you need to place a rush order, please call us by 11:00 a.m. Monday-Friday CST and ask for express service (allow 1-2 business days).

TECHNICAL ASSISTANCE

If you have questions, call our technical support line at 1-314-770-2228 between 8:00 a.m. and 5:00 p.m. Monday-Friday CST. Whether it involves design modifications or field assistance, our designers are extremely familiar with all of our designs and will be happy to help you. We want your home to be everything you expect it to be.

OTHER GREAT PRODUCTS

THE LEGAL KIT -

Avoid many legal pitfalls and build your home with confidence using the forms and contract featured in this kit. Included are request for proposal documents, various fixed price and cost plus contracts, instructions on how and when to use each form, warranty statements and more. Save time and money before you break ground on your new home or start a remodeling project. All forms are reproducible. The kit is ideal for homebuilders and contractors. **Cost: $35.00**

DETAIL PLAN PACKAGES -

Electrical, Plumbing and Framing Packages

Three separate packages offer homebuilders details for constructing various foundations; numerous floor, wall and roof framing techniques; simple to complex residential wiring; sump and water softener hookups; plumbing connection methods; installation of septic systems, and more. Each package includes three dimensional illustrations and a glossary of terms. Purchase one or all three. Note: These drawings do not pertain to a specific home plan.

Cost: $20.00 each or all three for $40.00

Plan Number	Square Feet	Price Code	Page	Right Read.
536-001D-0004	2,400	D	100	
536-001D-0005	2,820	E	182	
536-001D-0009	2,498	D	128	
536-001D-0011	3,200	F	110	
536-001D-0012	3,368	F	46	
536-001D-0014	2,401	D	29	
536-001D-0015	2,618	E	36	
536-001D-0017	2,411	D	72	
536-001D-0026	2,358	D	62	
536-001D-0027	2,328	D	189	
536-001D-0028	2,461	D	119	
536-001D-0032	2,520	D	216	
536-001D-0037	3,216	F	58	
536-001D-0038	3,144	E	87	
536-001D-0062	1,725	B	199	
536-001D-0094	3,360	H	241	
536-001D-0097	1,536	D	261	
536-001D-0098	1,536	D	274	
536-001D-0117	2,262	D	64	
536-001D-0118	2,511	D	217	
536-001D-0125	2,352	D	160	
536-003D-0003	2,501	D	167	
536-003D-0004	3,357	F	151	
536-006D-0002	3,222	F	159	
536-007D-0001	2,597	E	76	
536-007D-0002	3,814	G	184	
536-007D-0006	2,624	E	11	
536-007D-0007	2,523	D	30	
536-007D-0008	2,452	D	234	
536-007D-0009	2,716	E	211	
536-007D-0012	2,563	D	174	
536-007D-0016	3,850	F	203	
536-007D-0019	1,700	D	266	
536-007D-0020	2,318	F	251	
536-007D-0021	2,840	G	271	
536-007D-0022	4,240	H	253	
536-007D-0023	7,372	H	263	
536-007D-0024	2,986	G	275	
536-007D-0025	1,992	E	269	
536-007D-0026	1,704	D	242	
536-007D-0050	2,723	E	118	
536-007D-0051	2,614	E	66	
536-007D-0052	2,521	D	227	
536-007D-0057	2,808	F	25	
536-007D-0058	4,826	G	150	
536-007D-0059	3,169	F	9	
536-007D-0063	3,138	E	20	
536-007D-0066	2,408	D	139	
536-007D-0071	3,657	F	180	
536-007D-0072	2,900	E	235	
536-007D-0074	4,269	G	170	
536-007D-0076	3,666	H	246	
536-007D-0080	2,900	E	171	
536-007D-0082	3,034	E	101	
536-007D-0083	3,510	F	138	
536-007D-0084	3,420	F	106	
536-007D-0091	3,502	H	278	
536-007D-0092	2,901	E	247	
536-007D-0093	1,076	B	276	
536-007D-0094	2,408	F	280	
536-007D-0095	844	A	249	
536-007D-0096	2,986	E	262	
536-007D-0097	3,258	H	267	
536-007D-0098	2,397	D	143	
536-007D-0117	2,695	E	210	
536-007D-0132	3,861	F	18	
536-007D-0149	5,321	H	202	
536-007D-0152	3,670	F	104	
536-007D-0153	3,978	F	130	
536-007D-0158	3,974	F	111	
536-007D-0160	4,597	G	225	
536-007D-0165	3,352	F	238	
536-007D-0171	2,767	E	124	
536-007D-0182	3,269	F	113	
536-007D-0183	4,465	G	135	
536-007D-0186	2,859	E	221	
536-007D-0187	2,614	E	102	
536-007D-0190	3,056	D	245	
536-007D-0197	2,764	E	142	
536-007D-0202	6,088	H	149	
536-007D-0224	1,938	A	252	
536-007D-0230	1,923	D	185	
536-007D-0234	2,284	E	105	
536-008D-0002	2,678	E	207	
536-008D-0003	2,610	E	103	
536-008D-0007	2,662	G	265	
536-008D-0032	3,674	H	250	
536-008D-0033	4,936	H	256	
536-008D-0034	3,648	H	248	
536-008D-0036	2,360	D	191	
536-008D-0037	2,304	D	195	
536-008D-0038	2,518	D	114	
536-008D-0043	2,372	D	154	
536-008D-0051	3,641	F	108	
536-008D-0052	3,882	F	232	
536-008D-0058	3,013	E	196	
536-008D-0073	2,645	D	164	
536-008D-0075	2,406	D	146	
536-008D-0086	3,180	E	157	
536-008D-0087	2,324	D	233	
536-008D-0091	3,073	E	222	
536-008D-0092	3,073	E	198	
536-008D-0095	4,522	G	177	
536-008D-0100	3,066	G	277	
536-008D-0107	2,617	E	116	
536-008D-0108	2,602	E	236	
536-008D-0113	3,604	H	279	
536-008D-0114	2,010	E	258	
536-008D-0116	1,966	E	273	
536-008D-0118	1,924	E	254	
536-008D-0180	2,366	D	178	
536-013L-0031	2,253	D	152	•
536-013L-0033	2,340	D	115	
536-013L-0038	2,954	D	214	•
536-013L-0052	2,470	D	187	•
536-013L-0053	2,461	D	54	•
536-013L-0081	1,991	C	126	
536-013L-0108	2,897	D	136	•
536-013L-0116	3,271	E	229	
536-013L-0119	3,376	E	201	•
536-013L-0127	2,698	G	183	
536-013L-0128	2,760	G	237	
536-013L-0153	2,953	D	224	
536-013L-0157	2,964	D	212	•
536-013L-0178	3,770	E	80	•
536-013L-0179	3,159	D	39	•
536-014D-0003	3,003	E	140	
536-018D-0001	3,494	F	192	
536-018D-0002	3,169	E	144	
536-018D-0003	2,517	D	176	
536-018D-0007	2,696	E	91	
536-021D-0019	2,605	F	94	
536-022D-0028	2,223	D	70	
536-022D-0029	2,463	D	45	
536-022D-0030	3,412	F	213	
536-023D-0002	2,869	E	31	
536-023D-0003	2,824	E	50	
536-023D-0004	2,826	F	133	
536-023D-0005	2,672	E	73	
536-023D-0007	2,993	E	166	
536-023D-0008	2,801	E	218	
536-023D-0013	2,885	G	240	
536-023D-0014	4,184	H	259	
536-027D-0004	3,160	E	197	
536-027D-0008	3,411	F	190	
536-027D-0009	3,808	F	163	
536-027D-0014	4,288	F	21	
536-033D-0001	2,733	F	208	
536-033D-0002	1,859	D	60	
536-033D-0003	2,838	F	121	
536-033D-0006	3,019	F	125	
536-033D-0007	2,459	E	131	
536-037D-0023	3,503	F	204	
536-037D-0029	1,736	B	172	
536-037D-0030	2,397	D	112	
536-039L-0019	2,009	C	120	
536-039L-0021	2,148	C	129	
536-040D-0005	2,665	E	41	
536-040D-0009	2,468	D	158	
536-040D-0016	3,013	E	34	
536-040D-0017	3,072	E	231	
536-048D-0003	3,164	E	122	
536-048D-0004	2,397	E	78	
536-048D-0006	2,153	C	132	
536-048D-0007	3,290	F	141	
536-048D-0010	2,887	F	107	
536-051L-0020	2,491	D	109	
536-051L-0025	2,367	D	145	
536-051L-0067	2,649	F	175	
536-051L-0155	3,172	F	67	
536-051L-0189	3,109	G	47	
536-051L-0190	3,109	F	86	
536-051L-0246	3,113	F	23	
536-051L-0544	3,687	K	10	•
536-053D-0011	2,565	A	43	
536-053D-0012	2,356	B	19	
536-053D-0013	2,336	B	68	
536-053D-0014	2,195	A	134	
536-053D-0017	2,529	B	16	
536-053D-0018	2,583	B	38	
536-053D-0019	2,282	B	71	
536-053D-0020	2,773	B	49	
536-053D-0022	2,860	B	84	
536-053D-0023	2,895	B	56	
536-053D-0024	3,116	B	22	
536-053D-0025	3,017	B	33	
536-053D-0026	2,912	D	81	
536-053D-0027	4,120	D	74	
536-053D-0028	2,940	B	13	
536-053D-0034	2,846	B	89	
536-053D-0038	2,353	C	173	
536-053D-0054	3,315	F	137	
536-053D-0057	3,427	F	117	
536-053D-0059	2,511	C	179	
536-057D-0002	2,800	G	268	
536-057D-0005	1,044	AA	243	
536-057D-0006	1,966	E	272	
536-057D-0007	1,824	E	266	
536-057D-0015	1,626	D	257	
536-057D-0020	2,510	E	205	
536-058D-0001	2,830	G	270	
536-058D-0018	1,352	C	244	
536-058D-0028	896	A	252	
536-058D-0034	2,400	D	162	
536-058D-0035	3,267	F	215	•

(Continued, page 286)

Plan Number	Square Feet	Price Code	Page	Right Read.
536-058D-0039	2,240	D	193	•
536-058D-0040	2,200	D	156	
536-058D-0042	2,356	D	127	•
536-058D-0044	2,387	D	194	•
536-058D-0045	2,438	D	181	•
536-058D-0049	3,303	F	186	•
536-058D-0054	2,174	C	206	
536-058D-0057	3,061	E	169	•
536-058D-0071	2,830	G	264	
536-058D-0084	896	A	260	
536-058D-0092	2,547	D	200	
536-058D-0115	3,181	E	228	
536-058D-0117	3,528	F	148	
536-058D-0119	2,343	D	165	
536-058D-0121	2,218	D	226	
536-058D-0162	2,952	A	220	
536-058D-0165	2,558	B	230	
536-058D-0166	2,271	E	188	
536-065L-0003	2,816	E	96	
536-065L-0008	2,320	D	153	
536-065L-0009	2,403	D	95	
536-065L-0011	2,157	C	61	
536-065L-0012	2,738	E	82	
536-065L-0019	4,562	G	24	
536-065L-0024	4,652	G	57	•
536-065L-0036	2,587	D	123	•
536-065L-0043	3,816	F	51	•
536-065L-0073	2,484	D	161	•
536-065L-0077	4,328	G	28	•
536-065L-0078	3,421	F	48	•
536-065L-0087	3,688	F	44	•
536-065L-0120	5,143	H	14	
536-065L-0160	3,445	F	59	
536-065L-0208	3,793	F	32	•
536-065L-0210	4,517	G	63	•
536-065L-0214	3,809	F	37	
536-065L-0229	3,664	F	40	
536-065L-0230	4,160	G	92	
536-065L-0250	2,959	E	8	•
536-068D-0014	3,366	F	223	•
536-072L-0006	2,525	D	15	
536-072L-0019	3,195	G	17	
536-072L-0029	2,416	H	99	
536-072L-0030	2,396	E	65	
536-072L-0068	3,918	H	98	
536-072L-0321	3,107	G	52	
536-072L-0792	2,636	H	75	
536-072L-0794	3,196	G	77	
536-072L-0795	3,242	G	97	
536-072L-0841	2,356	E	79	
536-072L-0989	3,320	G	69	
536-072L-0994	3,265	G	55	
536-072L-1113	3,117	D	90	
536-072L-1115	3,117	D	35	
536-072L-1117	2,887	D	85	
536-072L-1116	3,000	D	83	
536-072L-1118	2,697	D	88	
536-072L-1119	2,858	D	12	
536-072L-1121	3,718	K	26	
536-072L-1122	2,525	D	53	
536-072L-1123	2,715	D	42	
536-072L-1126	2,908	D	93	
536-077L-0004	2,024	D	168	•
536-077L-0005	2,207	D	155	•
536-077L-0006	2,307	D	219	•
536-077L-0007	2,805	E	209	•
536-077L-0015	1,200	C	255	•
536-077L-0161	2,100	C	27	
536-121D-0004	3,782	E	147	•

EXCHANGE POLICIES

Since blueprints are printed in response to your order, we cannot honor requests for refunds. However, if for some reason you find that the plan you have purchased does not meet your requirements, you may exchange that plan for another plan in our collection within 90 days of purchase. At the time of the exchange, you will be charged a processing fee of 25% of your original plan package price, plus the difference in price between the plan packages (if applicable) and the cost to ship the new plans to you. Please note: Reproducible drawings can only be exchanged if the package is unopened.

BUILDING CODES & REQUIREMENTS

At the time the construction drawings were prepared, every effort was made to ensure that these plans and specifications meet nationally recognized codes. Our plans conform to most national building codes. Because building codes vary from area to area, some drawing modifications and/or the assistance of a professional designer or architect may be necessary to comply with your local codes or to accommodate specific building site conditions. We advise you to consult with your local building official for information regarding codes governing your area.

ADDITIONAL SETS*

Additional sets of the plan ordered are available for $45.00 each. Five-set, eight-set, and reproducible packages offer considerable savings.

MIRROR REVERSE PLANS*

Available for an additional $15.00 per set, these plans are simply a mirror image of the original drawings causing the dimensions and lettering to read backwards. Therefore, when ordering mirror reverse plans, you must purchase at least one set of right-reading plans. Some of our plans are offered mirror reverse right-reading. This means the plan, lettering and dimensions are flipped but read correctly. To purchase a mirror reverse right-reading set, the cost is an additional $150.00. See the Home Plans Index on pages 285-286 for availability.

ONE-SET STUDY PACKAGE

We offer a one-set plan package so you can study your home in detail. This one set is considered a study set and is marked "not for construction." It is a copyright violation to reproduce blueprints.

* Available only within 90 days after purchase of plan package or reproducible masters of the same plan.

BLUEPRINT PRICE SCHEDULE

Price Code	1-Set	Save $80 5-Sets	Save $115 8-Sets	Reproducible/ PDF File
AAA	$310	$410	$510	$610
AA	$410	$510	$610	$710
A	$470	$570	$670	$770
B	$530	$630	$730	$830
C	$585	$685	$785	$885
D	$635	$735	$835	$935
E	$695	$795	$895	$995
F	$750	$850	$950	$1050
G	$1000	$1100	$1200	$1300
H	$1100	$1200	$1300	$1400
I	$1150	$1250	$1350	$1450
J	$1200	$1300	$1400	$1500
K	$1250	$1350	$1450	$1550

Plan prices are subject to change without notice.
Please note that plans and material lists are not refundable.

SHIPPING & HANDLING CHARGES

US SHIPPING (AK and HI express only)

	1-4 Sets	5-7 Sets	8 Sets or Reproducibles
Regular (allow 7-10 business days)	$15.00	$17.50	$25.00
Priority (allow 3-5 business days)	$35.00	$40.00	$45.00
Express* (allow 1-2 business days)	$50.00	$55.00	$60.00

CANADA SHIPPING (to/from)**

	1-4 Sets	5-7 Sets	8 Sets or Reproducibles
Standard (allow 8-12 business days)	$35.00	$40.00	$45.00
Express* (allow 3-5 business days)	$75.00	$85.00	$95.00

*For express delivery please call us by 11:00 a.m. Monday-Friday CST
Overseas Shipping/International - Call, fax, or e-mail (plans@hdainc.com
for shipping costs.

**Orders may be subject to custom's fees and or duties/taxes

Note: Shipping and handling does not apply for PDF files.Orders will
be emailed within 24 hours (Mon.-Fri., 8am-5pm CST) of purchase

CAD FORMAT PLANS Many of our plans are available in CAD.
For availability, please call our Customer Service Number below.

1-877-379-3420

1.) **CALL** toll-free 1-877-379-3420 for credit card orders
2.) **FAX** your order to 1-314-770-2226
3.) **MAIL** the Order Form to: *HDA , Inc.*
944 Anglum Road
St. Louis, MO 63042
ATTN: Customer Service Dept.

For fastest service, Call Toll-Free
1-877-379-3420 day or night

ORDER FORM

Please send me -

PLAN NUMBER 536-_____

PRICE CODE _____ (see pages 285-286)

Specify Foundation Type (see plan page for availability)

☐ Slab   ☐ Crawl space   ☐ Pier

☐ Basement   ☐ Walk-out basement

☐ Reproducible Masters $_____

☐ PDF File Format $_____

☐ CAD Package (call for availability and pricing) $_____

☐ Eight-Set Plan Package $_____

☐ Five-Set Plan Package $_____

☐ One-Set Study Package (no mirror reverse) $_____

Additional Plan Sets*

☐ ____ (Qty.) at $45.00 each $_____

Mirror Reverse*

☐ Right-reading $150 one-time charge $_____
(see index on pages 285-286 for availability)

☐ Print in Mirror Reverse $_____
(where right-reading is not available)

____ (Qty.) at $15.00 each

☐ Legal Kit (see page 284) (002D-9991) $_____

Detail Plan Packages: (see page 284)

☐ Framing   ☐ Electrical   ☐ Plumbing
(002D-9992)   (002D-9993)   (002D-9994)

SUBTOTAL $_____

Sales Tax (MO residents add 7%) $_____

☐ Shipping / Handling (see chart on page 287) $_____

TOTAL (US funds only - sorry no CODs) $_____

I hereby authorize HDA, Inc. to charge this purchase to my credit card account (check one):

☐ MasterCard   ☐ VISA   ☐ DISCOVER   ☐ AMERICAN EXPRESS Cards

Prices are subject to change without notice.
Please note plans and material lists are not refundable.

Credit Card number_____

Expiration date _____

Signature _____

Name _____
(Please print or type)

Street Address _____
(Please do not use a PO Box)

_____

City_____

State_____

Zip_____

Daytime phone number   (_____) -_____

E-mail address _____

I am a   ☐ Builder/Contractor
☐ Homeowner
☐ Renter

I ☐ have ☐ have not selected my general contractor.

Thank you for your order!

* Available only within 90 days after purchase of plan package or reproducible masters of the same plan.

Note: Shipping and handling does not apply for PDF files. Orders will be emailed within 24 hours (Mon.-Fri., 8am-5pm CST) of purchase.